MENDELEYEV AND HIS PERIODIC TABLE

Dmitri Ivanovitch Mendeleyev

Born: February 8, 1834
Died: January 20, 1907

The world of chemistry could not have made the enormous strides it has made had it not been for Mendeleyev's discovery of the periodic table in 1869. It replaced confusion with order in the knowledge of the known elements and established a basic law of modern chemistry. This was a remarkable achievement for a young man in his thirties. He died at seventy-three, after a lifetime of varied accomplishments—as a teacher of remarkable skill; as a fighter for social justice; as a scientist who helped develop Russia's natural resources and whose prediction of three unknown elements was proven within fifteen years after the acceptance of his periodic table. Element 101, created in 1955, is called mendelevium in honor of Mendeleyev.

BOOKS BY ROBIN McKOWN

Biography

PAINTER OF THE WILD WEST
Frederic Remington

SHE LIVED FOR SCIENCE
Irène Joliot-Curie

GIANT OF THE ATOM
Ernest Rutherford

MENDELEYEV AND HIS PERIODIC TABLE

Fiction

AUTHORS' AGENT

JANINE

THE ORDEAL OF ANNE DEVLIN

MENDELEYEV
and his
PERIODIC
TABLE

by

Robin McKown

JULIAN MESSNER
NEW YORK

Published by Julian Messner
Division of Pocket Books, Inc.
8 West 40 Street, New York 10018

Second Printing, 1966

Printed in the United States of America
Library of Congress Catalog Card No. 65–12950

To Clyde with gratitude

ACKNOWLEDGMENTS

This is to express my gratitude to all those who assisted me in the gathering of informational background for this book. In particular, I am deeply indebted to Daniel Q. Posin, American scientist, teacher and scientific writer, who graciously permitted me to draw from the factual material in his own monumental novel about the life of Mendeleyev.

Robin McKown

TABLE OF CONTENTS

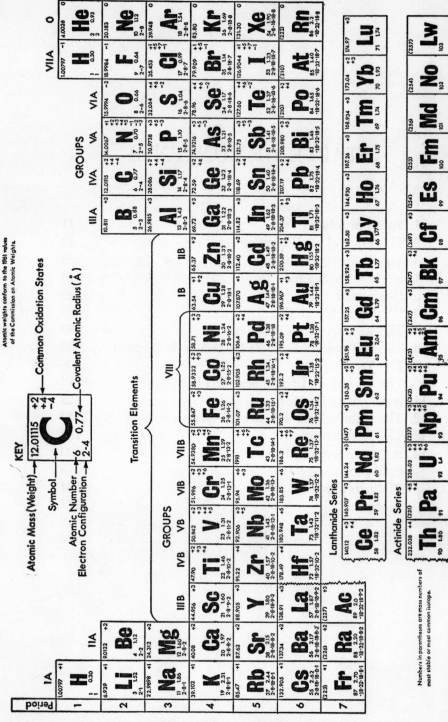

Periodic Table as Used Today

1

YOUTH IN SIBERIA

"MITYA," HIS FAMILY CALLED HIM, THOUGH HIS FULL NAME was Dmitri Ivanovitch Mendeleyev. He was born in the Western Siberian town of Tobolsk on February 8, 1834, the youngest of fourteen children. His father, a big, blond, hearty man of unusual intelligence, was director of the Tobolsk high school. The family was not wealthy but they lacked for nothing.

As Mitya grew into a strong and healthy baby, misfortune came to them. His father's world grew dim and dark until total blindness overtook him. The high school needed a director with two good eyes, and Ivan Pavlovitch Mendeleyev had no choice but to resign his post. The small pension granted him could not by any strategy be stretched to feed them all.

The wolf of hunger was, quite accidentally, evicted by Mitya's Uncle Vassili, the brother of his mother. Vassili Korniliev, who lived in Moscow, owned a small and run-down glass factory in the village of Aremziansk, seventeen miles from Tobolsk. He wrote his sister, asking her to recommend a capable manager who would undertake making the factory a paying proposition. She recommended herself. Knowing his sister was no ordinary woman, he agreed to give her the job. The whole family moved to Aremziansk.

"She is a fine woman, your mother," said Mitya's father, out of his pride in her, and out of his own despair. "The one good thing the Tartars left us."

Maria Dmitrievna, Mitya's black-haired handsome mother, had an interesting background. Her Russian father had been the publisher of Siberia's first newspaper, started in 1789 and called *Irtysch* after a river that ran through Tobolsk. She also had Tartar blood. The Tartars, under Genghis Khan, had invaded Siberia and part of Russia in the thirteenth century. After their defeat by Siberian Cossacks, many of the former conquerors stayed on as peaceful peasants. An ancestor of Maria's had married a Tartar beauty. Some of her family had the dark straight hair, narrow eyes and high cheekbones of the Mongols. Mitya, like his father, was blond and blue-eyed. But even as a child, he had his mother's fiery temperament and determination.

When Mitya was three, his father went to Moscow for an operation to remove the cataracts that clouded his vision. He returned months later. The operation had been partially successful. Ivan Pavlovitch Mendeleyev could recognize the faces of his children, though he could not read the small print of books. Soon afterward he developed the symptoms of tuberculosis, the dread enemy that rarely missed a household in the frozen north. Mitya always knew him as an invalid.

In Aremziansk, life settled down to a routine. Mitya's mother rose early, prepared breakfast and, before she left for work, embraced her youngest son, telling him to behave himself in her absence. While she was gone, Mitya's ailing father taught him to read and write and told him tales of Russia's heroic past. In pleasant weather, he often tagged after his older brothers and sisters on their trips to the woods to hunt for berries and nuts. He was interested in everything—pine cones, flowers, insects, birds, squirrels, rabbits—and later chattered incessantly to his mother about all these wonders of the world of nature.

One day the children tramped through the laurel trees and sweet-smelling cedars to the top of a high knoll. In the distance was the silhouette of the Ural Mountains.

"Look, Mitya," said his brother, Paul. "Over there, beyond the mountains, lies the real Russia."

"What is the real Russia?" Mitya asked.

"It is where the Tsar lives in a great palace," explained Paul. "In Russia the people dance and sing all day long. There is no sickness. The sun shines all the time and it is never cold."

Paul's idealistic portrait of "the real Russia"—in contrast to primitive Siberia—haunted Mitya for years.

With the energy born of necessity, Maria Dmitrievna brought life to the dying glass factory, sought new orders, employed more workmen, bought additional equipment. The great square wooden building with the huge smokestacks fascinated Mitya. By the time he was five or six, the glass factory was his second home. As he accompanied his mother on her daily rounds he bombarded her with questions.

In time he grew familiar with the sequence of activity. The sieves were filled with silica sand brought in from the hills by the draymen. Shaking the sieves rid the sand of iron and other impurities. Certain things were added and the sandy mixture went into the furnaces. At a high temperature, it was transformed into a molten mass.

"Why?" he asked.

"When it gets hot enough, it melts," the furnaceman told him, shrugging.

Mitya pondered. "Like ice in the sun?"

"Exactly."

With awe and wonder he watched the glass blower, stripped to the waist, blowing through an iron pipe into a white-hot glob from the furnace, swinging and revolving the pipe, then blowing again—to make goblets, bottles, pharmaceutical instruments and the long cylinders that would later be flattened into windowpanes.

"How does he do it, Mother?"

"It is an art and a skill, Mitya. It takes patience and practice."

On a shelf he saw laid out the vividly colored glass for stained glass windows.

"Red, blue, yellow, green," he enumerated on his fingers. "How beautiful! What makes the glass so many colors?"

Smiling and proud, his mother beckoned to the old chemist. "My son wants to understand the coloring process. Would you explain it to him?"

"It is done with chemicals," the old man said. Gravely, he led the small boy to the metal trays with his coloring materials. "Sit down now and watch." In turn he took a pinch of powder from each tray and set fire to it, producing varicolored flames. Entranced, Mitya asked more questions, repeated the answers.

That night, as they ate their supper of steaming borsch and hot meat pies, he showed off his new knowledge.

"Oxides of chromium will make green glass," he said. "Manganese oxide is for violet—or for pink or amethyst, depending on how much we use. Purple comes from potassium. For red panes of glass, we must add copper oxide. Cobalt oxide is for blue, and iron oxide for yellow."

His father choked into his soup. Liza, his youngest sister, stared in astonishment, her spoon poised halfway to her lips.

"I don't yet know why this is," Mitya added honestly. "When I am older, I will find out."

His mother gathered him into her arms. "Mitya is the brightest of all of you. If it kills me, I am going to see that he gets the best education in the world."

His brothers and sisters could have been jealous at this favoritism; instead they lavished affection on him, as their mother did. His father, from his own tragedy, could have pointed out that education was a one-way road, that books could only ruin one's eyes. Instead he passed on things he had learned to Mitya, delighted to see how well he listened and how quickly he learned.

When he was seven, his parents drove him to Tobolsk, where he was to live as a resident student in the primary school. It was the day of the town council, and as they approached the town, they heard its bell ringing to summon the members.

"Listen!" Mitya's father exclaimed. "Our bell is one of Siberia's first exiles, Mitya."

"How can a bell be an exile?" he demanded, skeptically.

His father explained, giving him a short history lesson at the same time.

Once the bell had hung in the belfry of the Russian town of Uglich, where the widow of Ivan the Terrible was living with her small son, Prince Dmitri. His older brother, Feodor, was Tsar of Russia, though Boris Godunov, a boyar, was acting regent until Feodor came of age. In 1593, the little Prince Dmitri was stabbed to death. Boris Godunov was suspected of the crime. Five years later, when Feodor died, Boris Godunov became Tsar, since there was no other heir. In the meantime, the whole town of Uglich was punished for Dmitri's murder. Many leading citizens were executed. The clapper of the bell which had rung the alarm was removed, while the bell itself was exiled to Siberia "for life"!

The people of Tobolsk gave the bell a new clapper. It had hung in their belfry ever since. Not long before, Uglich had requested its return, but the mayor of Tobolsk refused. The sentence had been "for life." As long as the bell could ring, he pointed out, its life was not over.

"All over Russia, Tobolsk is famed as the home of the Uglich bell," his father concluded.

His mother wanted to add, but dared not, that one day Tobolsk would be even more celebrated as the birthplace of "Mendeleyev, the scientist."

Mitya was lonely his first months away from home, cried himself to sleep, lived for the holidays when he could be reunited with his family and his friends of the glass factory. Gradually he became absorbed in his new life. From the first, his teachers were impressed with his quick mind and excellent memory. "When the time comes you must go to Moscow and study at its university," his professor of mathematics, I. K. Rummel, told him. "There one can find knowledge served up on a plate like a tempting soup."

Henceforth Mitya dreamed of going to Moscow, the city whose doctors had given back his father's eyesight, the city where men of vast learning taught in a shining university and there were books that had the answers to all the things he wanted to know. He shared his dream with his mother the next time he saw her. Thereafter they dreamed together, and, forgetting the fragile substance of a dream, gave theirs a reality as solid as a fact.

Outside of his regular professors, Mitya had a tutor assigned to guide him. This was a turbulent imaginative young classics scholar, Pyotr Yershov. Yershov's passion was folklore—the stories about dragons and witches and talking animals which the peasants told to each other in the long winter evenings. In his spare time he collected these stories and wrote them down in a little notebook. Once, when he and Mitya were walking in the forest outside of Tobolsk, he told him of the adventures of a peasant boy named Ivan who owned a little humpbacked horse of a most unusual disposition. Not only could the humpbacked horse talk and fly through the air with Ivan on his back, he managed to conjure for his small master riches and glory and a mighty kingdom and a princess to wed.

Mitya enjoyed made-up stories like this one, but he liked even better the real things he learned at school. All except Latin.

"Why must I study Latin?" he burst out to his tutor. "What use is it?"

Yershov patted his shoulders encouragingly. "You want to graduate, don't you? When the time comes, you'll have to know Latin so you can pass your examinations and be eligible for a university."

Still rebellious, Mitya struggled with the hated Latin verbs, but his marks remained discouragingly low in this subject.

From his schoolbooks Mitya learned that Tobolsk, the refuge of the Uglich bell-in-exile, was a market center for fish and furs, that it was founded in 1587, and that snow fell there on an average of fifty days a year. The schoolbooks did not mention that it was a receiving center for thousands of human exiles, on their way to hard labor in the remote and desolate regions of eastern Siberia.

At a gray and gloomy building known as "the forwarding prison" they arrived in convoys—thieves and murderers and others sentenced for the most trivial offenses, along with the political exiles whose crime was that they had voiced objections to the tyranny of the Tsar's rule.

One bitter winter day, when Mitya was walking through town with a schoolmate, their way was blocked by a long line of these exiles, dazed and stumbling with the terrible fatigue of a two-thousand-mile march from European Russia. Their shabby overcoats had a yellow diamond sewn on the back. They were barefoot or had their feet bound in rags, and there were fetters on their ankles and a chain reaching from ankles to waist. On one side their hair was shaven close, and beards and mustaches were half-shaven too, giving them an appearance both clownlike and pathetic. All were dirty, haggard and emaciated.

Some women of the town, tears streaming down their cheeks, rushed up to hand the prisoners bread and hard-boiled eggs. Guards pushed them back and the food fell to the ground, to be trampled in the snow and mud.

Mitya watched the scene with horror.

"Why must they suffer so?" he cried out.

It was another question to which no one could give him the answer.

The glass factory in Aremziansk, which Uncle Vassili had now deeded to his sister, became moderately prosperous. Mitya's mother employed a capable man as manager and did not have to oversee it daily. The family moved back to Tobolsk to join Mitya. Once more he could sleep under his own roof.

Their home was soon a gathering place for Tobolsk's intellectuals. This small group was expanded by certain political exiles who had served their sentence but were still not permitted to return to Russia. They often came from good families, were well educated and inevitably idealistic. The

Tobolsk gentry, starved for interesting conversation and creative ideas, did not think of them as condemned criminals but as distinguished visitors.

One of them came frequently to Mitya's home—a lean hawk-nosed man named Nicolai Bassargin, who was a Decembrist. The Decembrists were a group of young officers of the nobility who, in the early 1820's, had organized a secret society to fight for a constitutional monarchy and the liberation of Russia's approximately forty million serfs. On December 14, 1825—they owed their name to this date —they had staged a demonstration of soldiers in St. Petersburg against the new Tsar, Nicholas I. Frightened and angry, the young ruler ordered his artillery to disburse them. The Decembrists were arrested, five of their leaders were hanged, and more than a hundred, Bassargin among them, were sentenced to hard labor in the mines of eastern Siberia. In 1826, Bassargin had been part of a prison convoy like the one Mitya had seen.

Now a free settler, he seldom spoke of his frightful ordeal, though he was still deeply concerned with the rights of the Russian people for freedom and for education.

The reason for his visits to the Mendeleyev home was soon apparent. Mitya's attractive older sister, Olga, had returned there after the death of her first husband. Bassargin was deeply in love with her, and she grew to feel the same way about him. After their marriage they settled in nearby Yaloutorovsk, but Mitya continued to see them regularly. Between him and his new brother-in-law a strong bond grew.

Since his release, Bassargin had built up a sizable library, including many works from France and England that were forbidden in Russia. His passion was science, which he described to Mitya as the investigation of everything in the universe. Sometimes he spoke of the moon and the planets and the stars, talking of distances beyond comprehension. Again he mentioned atoms, incredibly small particles of which all matter was made. "There are many who still say that atoms are imaginary, Mitya, but do not listen to them. They are as real as this piece of wood."

Another time, he gestured toward the distant Urals. "Those mountains hide incalculable quantities of minerals, Mitya. Go south to Caucasia and you will find oil bubbling beneath the earth's surface. Minerals and oil—they are the riches of Russia. It is the scientist who will show how they can be used to free Russia of misery and despair."

Nothing Bassargin said impressed Mitya so deeply. Science, then, was not an end in itself. The scientist had the knowledge to make life better for everyone. He would like to be a scientist.

To Bassargin, Mitya could have been himself, as he was before the Siberian exile had blighted his career, and he shared the dream of sending Mitya to the University of Moscow. While his mother drilled Mitya in Latin conjugations, Bassargin coached him in history. Thus together they prepared him for the stiff competition they knew he must meet.

Then disaster struck, not once but again and again and again.

In 1847, Mitya's father at last succumbed to tuberculosis. That his death was not unexpected did not soften the shock of his loss. A few months later, the same malady took the oldest daughter. Most of Mitya's other brothers and sisters were married and scattered. There were only two children left in the family, now, Mitya and his frail sister Liza. The mother, as she had done before, put sorrow behind her.

On one of her inspection trips to the glass factory, she took Mitya with her.

"This is your future," she told her son, pointing to the rows upon rows of glassware and glass instruments in the stockroom. "Our glass will buy your university education."

Then one bitterly cold night in the winter of 1849 the factory caught fire and burned to the ground. Of the beautiful glass, there remained only a mass of tiny bright crystals mixed with rubble. Mitya wandered disconsolately through the ruins, thinking how the fire had also consumed his future. Bassargin, who had endured floggings and cold and hunger without flinching, suffered most of all. For months he went around scowling, a sneer of bitterness on his lips.

Mitya offered to give up his studies and get a job, but his mother insisted he finish high school.

"Who knows what will happen before then?" she demanded with forced cheerfulness. Changing the subject, she talked to Mitya about his father.

In his youth, she said, Ivan Pavlovitch was inordinately fond of horses, and his first job was as a horse trader. His real name was Solokov, but at this time people started to call him "Mendeleyev," from the two Russian words meaning "to change" and "business." At heart he was not a businessman, and he began to yearn for a chance to use his mind for more than selling and buying horses. One day he quit everything, made his way to St. Petersburg and entered as a student at the Pedagogical Institute. He studied philosophy, fine arts, logic and literature and, after his graduation, accepted a teaching position at Tobolsk, where he and Maria had met and married.

"So you see, Mitya, if you want something bad enough, there are ways . . ."

Vaguely encouraged, Mitya continued at school until the following June. Now a tall and husky youth of fifteen, he graduated with honors in all subjects but Latin, which he barely passed. He went home to give the news to his mother, Bassargin, Olga and Liza, who were all awaiting his arrival. They beamed at him.

"This requires a celebration," his mother said. "I have prepared your favorite—meat balls in cabbage leaves."

"Later, Mother. There is something I have to do first."

He darted out the door before anyone could stop him.

At a nearby street corner, a dozen or so of his fellow students were waiting for him. Laughing and boisterous, they marched beyond the outskirts of town, stopping under a large birch tree on a hill. At a signal each took from beneath his jacket a copy of Popov's *Latin Grammar*. One by one they laid the books on the ground beneath the birch tree and then tossed stones and dirt on them until they were covered. The ceremony over, they shook hands all around and set off for town. Latin, the dead language that had plagued them all their school years, had at long last received the burial it should have had, in their opinion, centuries before.

The fragrance of the meat balls and cabbage greeted Mitya as he entered his home for the second time that evening. Famished, he sat down at the table.

Bassargin rose from his seat by the stove. "Before you eat we have something to tell you," he said. "You didn't give us a chance before. Your mother has accomplished a miracle. From somewhere she has materialized enough money to get you to Moscow. You will be able to go to the university after all." He was smiling broadly, and suddenly unable to control himself, picked up his wife and whirled her around, chanting, "Life is wonderful."

As Mitya sat there dazed, his mother added, "Liza and I are going with you, my darling. There is nothing to keep us here any longer."

Bassargin stopped his gyrations. "You must take good care of them, Dmitri," he said, for the first time using his real name instead of his pet nickname. "Another thing I must warn you. The Latin examination they will give you for your entrance examinations will be much stiffer than the one you took here. You will have to cram on Latin all summer long."

No one could understand why Mitya burst out laughing.

2

THE PRICE OF AN EDUCATION

In 1849 Russia's first major railroad—between St. Petersburg and Moscow—was under construction. There were still no railroads in all the vast stretches of Siberia. Some fifteen years previously a plan for a comprehensive network of railways had been proposed to the Minister of Finance, but he rejected it on the grounds that trains would be a threat to "public morals." Railways, he said, "encouraged frequent purposeless travel, thus fostering the restless spirit of our age."

Rich people traveled in their own carriages, and for those of moderate means there were droshkies or stagecoaches. Mitya, Liza and their mother, who had to count their pennies, set out on the 1500-mile journey from Tobolsk to Moscow in a telega, a small one-horse cart without springs and with only one seat in front for the driver. For two women and one youth, not yet full grown, it was a brave and bold undertaking. Luckily they had a sturdy horse. Called Soldier, he was a gift of friends in Aremziansk.

Mitya alternated with his mother in the driver's seat. The rest of the time he sat in the back of the cart with Liza, who was not strong enough to handle Soldier. All the house-

24

hold treasures they could not bear to leave behind were piled around them.

Day after day they traveled through deep pine forests and barren rolling steppes, across swamps and rivers and meadows. If fortune was smiling, they found a post station at nightfall. This was usually a small hut where the proprietor offered them black bread and warm milk and permitted them to sleep on top of the large clay stove or on the floor wrapped in their own blankets. When no post station was in sight, the women slept in the back of the telega while Mitya stretched out on the ground or a makeshift bed of pine boughs.

They did their cooking over a campfire and made hot black tea in the teakettle, which no Russian travelers, rich or poor, were ever without. At night when his mother and Liza were asleep, Mitya sat by the flickering fire, a book open before him. It was an advanced Latin grammar, Bassargin's last present to him. He was determined to master the language which he now believed to be the only possible barrier between him and the University of Moscow.

One day Soldier took them up a muddy treacherous road across the Ural Mountains. On the other side they descended into European Russia. Its neat farms and villages of wooden houses with carved and decorated gables were in vivid contrast to the wild stretches of Siberia. It was Sunday, and laughing peasant girls in their best finery and muzhiks (peasant farmers) in bright red blouses and black velvet trousers waved at them as they passed. "A land where people dance and sing all day long." Paul's words rang over the years. But as the days passed, Mitya was aware that there was poverty here just as in Siberia, and serfs, rare in Siberia, were treated by their masters with less care than cattle or horses.

They crossed the Volga, dense with barges and boats, and at last the domes and cupolas of Moscow rose abruptly before them. They had traveled all summer long.

"Golden-headed Moscow!" Mitya was speechless with wonder. It was dusk, the time of vespers, and all around them bells pealed and clanged their call to the faithful from the city's four hundred churches with their golden spires. Though Peter the Great had moved the capital to his city, St. Petersburg, for the vast majority of Russians and Siberians "Mother Moscow" was still the center of the world.

One after another they drove past the walls built for the city's defense. The Siberians gazed awestruck at the great houses, the painted and gilded carriages, escorted by guards in scarlet livery and turbans, and all the people on the crowded streets—bearded priests, soldiers clad in striking and varied uniforms, street vendors crying their wares, beautiful women in bonnets trimmed with feathers. If anyone smiled at the sight of the odd vehicle from Siberia and their country appearance, they were unaware of it.

"Would you believe it, Mother? The Tartars burned Moscow to the ground in 1571. Now look at it." Mitya was thinking of the fire at the glass factory and what a fearful calamity it had seemed at the time.

They reached the stone walls surrounding the Kremlin, the group of palaces, cathedrals and official buildings which were the heart and lifeblood of Moscow. The great Spasski gate, topped by a glittering double-headed golden eagle, stood wide open, and they paused for a glimpse of the splendor within. Timidity kept them from venturing farther.

"We had better ask directions to your uncle's house," Maria murmured. Her eyes were glowing.

Much later that evening, after a long search and many wrong turns, they found his mansion. Uncle Vassili greeted

Maria with the proper warmth due a sister he had not seen for years and welcomed her children. Generously he assured them that his house would be theirs for the length of the stay. But when they confided the reason for their presence, he shook his head.

In his opinion, university training was a waste of time. He had never had an education and had managed very well without it. Why not let him get Dmitri a post in a government office? With luck and diligence, he could carve a career for himself and become a rich man.

"I appreciate your offer, Uncle," Dmitri said politely and firmly. "But my mind is made up. Nothing will make me change it."

The next morning mother and son were standing before the stern-faced Registrar of the university. He gazed indifferently at the tall dark-haired woman in her peasant embroidered blouse and at the blond tanned youth with deep blue eyes fixed on him as though he were king of the universe.

"What can I do for you?"

"I would like my son to take the examinations for a government scholarship," Maria said.

He examined the papers from the Tobolsk high school which she thrust into his hands.

"Impossible," he announced abruptly. "Utterly impossible. Your son did not graduate from a high school in the Moscow district and is therefore not eligible to take the examinations for a scholarship or to enter the university on any basis whatsoever."

His terrible words fell like hailstones, blasting their long-nourished dream. Neither of them could believe him. Maria spoke of her son's high grades in Tobolsk, quoted his professors as saying that they had never before had a student of such extraordinary brilliance and prodigious memory. Uneasy at her stream of praise, Dmitri interrupted to beg for, or rather to insist on, a chance to show that he could hold his own with students from the Moscow district. They could both have saved their breath.

"I have told you," the Registrar said, scowling. "It is against regulations. There is nothing I can do. Absolutely nothing." He ushered them to the door.

They walked slowly through the winding, bustling streets toward Uncle Vassili's home. Dmitri was too depressed to speak.

"Never mind, Mitya." Maria's voice was calm now, giving no hint that their world was shattered into fragments. "We will go to St. Petersburg and apply there. If that doesn't succeed, we will try elsewhere. You are going to a university and it will be a good one."

Dmitri turned to stare at his mother, seeing her fine profile, the lines of strain in her forehead, the unnatural flush of her cheeks. "How courageous you are, Mother! How very determined!"

"Those qualities I bequeath to you," she said lightly. "We must tell my brother that we will be leaving in a few days so that you can be enrolled this year."

Destiny decided otherwise. Liza fell sick with a fever. The doctor told them it would be months before she could travel. There was no alternative but to spend the winter in Moscow. While Maria looked after her daughter, Dmitri spent his time in the Moscow libraries. Despite his lack of sympathy with book learning, Uncle Vassili was tolerant and kind. At last spring came. With the first days of warm sunshine, Liza's health took a turn for the better. It was time for the small family to move on.

Their money was nearly gone, and when they refused a loan, Uncle Vassili had his servant load their telega with supplies. Because discouragement had struck their hearts, the five-hundred-mile journey to St. Petersburg seemed endless. Maria grew haggard, beset with unfamiliar aches and pains which she did her best to conceal. The constant jolting in the back of the telega was almost unbearable to Liza, although she did not complain either.

Finally they reached their destination, the city built on the swamps in 1703 by Peter the Great. "A window to Europe," he had called St. Petersburg. Its architecture combined Dutch stairstep roofs, the ornate detail of the Germans, French symmetry and a purely Russian love of color. The public buildings along the Neva, including the vast Winter Palace of the Emperor, were splendid beyond belief. The grim Fortress of St. Paul and St. Peter, on an island in the river, held prisoners condemned to a living death—and also a church with the tallest spire in all of Russia.

There was no time for sightseeing. They rented a couple of shabby rooms in the humblest district of the city, and the very next day Dmitri applied for entrance in the Medico-Surgical Institute, determined to try any and all colleges in the hope of getting into one. It was a relief to be turned down. He did not want to be a doctor.

"Bassargin has a friend here," Dmitri told his mother, "a professor of chemistry at the university, Nicolai N. Zinin. He told me to seek him out if ever I got this far."

They found Professor Zinin in his office at the university, a slight youngish man, beardless but with the most remarkable mustaches Dmitri had ever seen. Swept into a large curl on each side, they reached almost to his collarbone.

"Bassargin?" he demanded eagerly. "He is well? How

often I have thought of him—knowing, of course, the reason
he would never write. A brilliant man. A great loss to
science, his . . . departure."

"He is married to my daughter," Maria explained. "He
has tutored my son, unofficially, of course. He says Dmitri
has a fine mind." She spoke impersonally. "I'm sure my
son-in-law would want him to study with you."

"You are interested in chemistry, my boy?"

"Yes," said Dmitri, adding for the sake of accuracy. "At
Tobolsk we studied mainly physics and mathematics."

Zinin smiled. "The three are inseparable. So Lomonosov
said. You have heard of Lomonosov?"

Dmitri nodded. "Bassargin told me about him. A scientist,
a poet and an artist, was he not?"

"A great scientist." Zinin spoke emphatically. "A century
in advance of his time he foresaw Dalton's atomic theory."
He was leafing through an old book. "Listen. This is what I
wanted you to hear. 'Eyes are useless to a person who wants
to see the inside of a thing, but has no hands to open it.
Hands are useless to a person who has no eyes to see the
inside of a thing even when it is open. Chemistry may be
called the hands of physics, and mathematics—its eyes.'

"If you want to be a scientist, Dmitri Ivanovitch, you
must master all three—chemistry, physics and mathematics."

"I will try, sir." His heart was full of pride that this professor should address him as men did their equals, "Dmitri
Ivanovitch."

"As for entering the university," Zinin continued, "unfortunately I have little to say. You will have to see the
Director, Ivan Pletnov. I will give you a note to him, though
it is of small value . . ."

"Did you say Pletnov?" interrupted Maria.

"Yes," he said. "I must warn you above all not to mention Bassargin. Not to anybody. The memory of the Decembrists is a raw wound to the authorities. They seek students who will not make trouble. It is not easy. Youth these days is burning with revolutionary ideas. How do you feel?"

"I burn with the desire to learn," Dmitri told him.

"Pletnov," Maria repeated, when they left the professor. "Ivan Pletnov. I wonder . . ."

They made their way to the office of the Director. Dmitri noticed that his mother's step was unusually light.

"Tell Director Pletnov," she said to the attendant, "that the widow of Ivan Pavlovitch Mendeleyev is here."

"He knew Father?" Dmitri demanded, after the attendant had departed with the message.

"Your father's best friend in his student days was named Ivan Pletnov," she confided. "We shall soon know if this is the same man."

Barely had she spoken when the Director stormed out of his office, embraced Maria in the name of her husband and wept at the news of his death. Presently, Maria introduced Dmitri and explained why they were there. Pletnov asked him a few questions, but it was obvious he was already convinced that the son of his old friend must have the qualifications of a scholar. He would speak to the Minister of Education himself about a scholarship, he promised. To be sure, that was only the first step. There were innumerable papers to be filled out and a string of government and scholastic personages whose approval must be obtained. Were they willing to go through all that?

"If we must," Maria agreed quickly.

Weeks later, in the fall of 1850, with papers duly made out and approved, Dmitri was permitted to take his examinations. The questions were long and detailed, embracing physics, mathematics, chemistry, biology, geography, literature, history and the inevitable Latin. He passed everything, including Latin. Even so, he was not admitted to the university proper, but to the Pedagogical (teacher training) Institute, where his father had studied. Although the institute was theoretically apart from the university, it occupied the same buildings, and many professors taught in both the university and institute.

As a scholarship student, Dmitri would live at the institute. Room, board, clothes and books were all provided. In return he was expected to teach for eight years after graduation, a condition he accepted readily. At last the dream had come true, not in the way they had dreamed it to be sure, but close enough to fill him with the wildest exuberation.

At the end of his first week of classes, he paid a visit to his mother and Liza, bounding up the steps to their attic rooms two at a time. They were sitting quietly sewing when he strode in, but they jumped up immediately and embraced him.

"How splendid you look, Mitya." His mother blissfully fingered the material of his new school uniform. "My university student! *Akh*, how proud I am!"

Liza took his student cap with its regulation blue band, handling it as reverently as a sacred relic. "You must tell us everything. From the beginning." She scurried to light the fire under the teakettle.

Dmitri sat down, stretching his long legs, relishing the chance to confide to the two people he loved so dearly.

The institute had two faculties, he told them. The historical-philological dealt with fine arts. The other, physical-mathematical, included the sciences. Naturally he had chosen most of his courses in the latter group.

On his fingers he named those courses and their professors. Stepan Kuforga was his geology professor. Physics was under Professor Emil Lenz and mathematics under Mikhail Ostragradsky. Professor Ruprecht taught him botany. He would learn zoology from Professor F. Brandt, and Savitch, the astronomer, would initiate him in that subject. They were all famous men in their fields, the best in Russia.

Though he would be allowed to sit in on the chemistry lectures of Professor Zinin, Bassargin's friend, his regular chemistry professor was A. A. Voskresensky. "What a man he is!" A droll, pudgy little fellow in appearance, but his brilliance was undeniable as was his gift for inspiring his pupils to do their best.

"Think boldly," Voskresensky had told them. "When you encounter obstacles, tackle them one by one. Don't let the difficulties of scientific work discourage you. Remember, it is not the gods who bake the pots and make the bricks."

Ever since he was a child watching the old chemist at the glass factory, chemistry had been a tantalizing word to him. Now he was sure it was his chosen field.

"Chemistry," he quoted, "is the science of transformations of substances into other substances."

Liza and his mother were listening intently, but he could see their bewilderment.

"Take water," he said, seeking the simplest example. "Water is a liquid but it is made up of two elements, hydrogen and oxygen, which are both gas."

"How fascinating!" exclaimed Liza. "And sometimes water is snow and sometimes ice or rain or a waterfall or a cool spring—or steam from a boiling teakettle . . ." She ran to make her tea. "Is that what you mean?"

"Not exactly," said Dmitri, smiling. "Water in different forms is still water. There are hundreds of thousands of substances in the world." He looked around. "Sugar and salt and wood and china and glass . . . I could go on forever. But all of them are made of elements, of which we know about forty. There are certainly more. Elements," he quoted again, "are substances made up only of themselves."

His mother was sitting bolt upright in her chair, her gaze fixed brightly on her son, an aura of contentment about her, in this, the happiest and proudest moment of her life. Liza, pale and wraithlike, seemed unable to contain herself. A loaf of bread and a knife in her hand, she swirled around, stopping directly in front of her brother.

"But how?" she demanded, her voice breathless with excitement. "How can hundreds of thousands of things be made from just forty elements?"

"They unite," he explained gently. "They unite in different combinations. You see, Liza, every element is made up of infinitely small particles, not visible to the naked eye. 'Corpuscles,' Lomonosov called them in the last century, though John Dalton—he was an Englishman—called them atoms, as did the ancient Greeks. Atoms or molecules." He was not very sure of this point. "It was Dalton's theory that the atoms of different elements have different weights. Hydrogen has very light atoms, for instance, and iron has quite heavy ones. Atoms from two or more elements unite to form a larger particle, and then one has a substance completely different from the original elements."

"Unbelievable," murmured Liza. "Almost unbelievable."

"The air is a mixture of gas elements," he continued, "hydrogen and oxygen and nitrogen. Mercury is a liquid element. Some elements are metals so soft you can bend them. Then there are gold and silver and copper, which are all hard and shiny and beautiful. It is a curious thing how some elements are so much alike and others so very different."

As he drank the hot tea and ate the bread and jam Liza put before him, he chattered on, reeling off the things he had learned, basking in the adoring glances of these two women for whom he was the entire world.

"You have mastered all this so quickly." His mother was beside herself with pride.

"It's really very little," Dmitri confessed. "I'm going to have to work very hard. At my age Voskresensky was studying with Justin Liebig of Munich, the man who founded agricultural chemistry. Liebig told his students, 'If you plan to be a chemist you must be prepared to ruin your health by hard study; nothing less will produce anything.'" Seeing his mother's distressed expression, Dmitri added hastily. "Naturally, he exaggerated a little. Liebig's laboratory, by the way, was known as 'a factory for the production of professors.' In my opinion, Voskresensky is the very best professor that 'factory' produced. . . ."

He was interrupted by a fit of coughing from Liza, which she vainly tried to control.

"How selfish I am," he cried, leaping to her side. "You are ill again, little sister. And I . . . thinking only of myself."

She pressed a handkerchief to her mouth. "It is nothing. A cold. It will pass. The climate here . . ."

"Yes, the climate," her mother echoed. "The wet, damp climate of St. Petersburg on the marshes. Your father often spoke of it." But she sounded frightened.

"You are not well either." He looked at her closely and noticed her flushed swollen face. "How are you going to get along? Have you enough money?" He emptied his pockets, almost apologetically. "They give me a little change for incidentals. I wish it were more."

"Keep it." His mother's voice was firm. "You're not to worry about us. We'll manage."

"Perhaps it was a mistake," he burst out wildly. "I could quit school, go to work, look after the two of you . . ."

"And break my heart?" Maria demanded. "You would not be so cruel. Go back to your school, Mitya. That is where you belong."

He went—not without misgivings—but his fears were pushed into the background by the feast of knowledge now set before him, knowledge he devoured with all the hunger of his eager young mind. Yet it could not escape him on his weekly visits home that illness had come to stay.

One morning a young boy who lived in the same house with Maria and Liza slipped into his classroom and whispered to him that he must come at once. Liza, weeping, met him at the door.

"Mother," she sobbed. "I think she's holding on just so she can see you again."

Stunned with horror, he followed her into the kitchen.

A doctor was there and drew Dmitri aside. "A remarkable woman," he said. "With her ailment—it is dropsy—it seems incredible she has lasted this long. She wants to talk to you. Go in now."

She lay there so still, her head propped up on pillows, her eyes closed. He stood motionless, scarcely daring to breathe, but she heard him, looked up and smiled.

"They called you from your studies, Mitya. What a pity!"

"Mother, I did not know," he stammered, twisting his cap in his hand. "Why did you tell me nothing?"

"Come closer, my darling." Her voice seemed far away. "I want to talk to you."

"Yes, little Mother." He knelt beside her, pressing his hand to her forehead.

"Listen, carefully," she said. "Avoid illusions. Know that in work and not words alone your path lies. Continue always to seek patiently divine truth—and scientific truth. You will not forget?"

"No, *Mamashka*," he said, choking.

"You were the youngest and my favorite," she murmured faintly. "Perhaps that was wrong, but I could not help it. You will go further than the others. . . ." Her voice faded away.

Liza had come in softly and was kneeling in a corner before the icon. Now she rose and brought a lighted candle to the bedside, placing it between her mother's hands. Maria Dmitrievna Mendeleyev lived only a few hours longer.

"Work and not words alone . . . seek patiently divine truth—and scientific truth . . . avoid illusions."

His mother's last command rang in Dmitri's ears constantly the next months, as he drove himself to his studies in a vain effort to blot out his grief.

After Maria's death, Liza moved to a smaller room. To pay her rent, she took in sewing from her neighbors. Dmitri sold their telega and the faithful Soldier to help support her and visited her as often as he could, but in her gentle way she tried to discourage his visits. Her coughing spells were increasing. She wished to spare him the pain of seeing her fading health. A few months after they had lost their mother, Liza too was gone. Tuberculosis had taken another victim from their family. Dmitri was alone.

Liza was buried in Volkovo Cemetery, at the side of Maria. A soft snow fell during the simple ceremony. The snowflakes lighting on Dmitri's dark jacket, exquisite in design and varied as nature itself, glistened briefly before dissolving into moisture, a symbol of the ephemeral quality of all living things.

Afterward he walked at random up and down the silent white streets. At length he found himself in Senate Square, beneath the great equestrian statue of Peter the Great, which had been done by a French sculptor, Falconnet, and about which the Russian poet Pushkin had written "The Bronze Horseman."

It was here, twenty-five years before—December 14, 1825 —that the Decembrists had staged their famous demonstration. How often had Bassargin described it! In his mind he saw the battalion of soldiers, standing rigidly hour after hour, refusing to take the oath of allegiance to Nicholas I, demanding "Constantine!" the older brother of Nicholas whom they considered the rightful Tsar, and "A constitution!"—only to be shot down like cattle.

How futile their sacrifice was, he told himself bitterly, thinking in truth of the two women who had sacrificed their lives so that he, Dmitri Ivanovitch Mendeleyev, could study at a university.

That night he wrote to Bassargin, telling him all that had happened. His own brothers and sisters were widely scattered. In his misery, it seemed to him that his brother-in-law was now his only link to the past.

3

THE UNIVERSITY STUDENT

"RELEASE DOSTOEVSKY!" SHOUTED THE STUDENTS IN FRONT OF the university. "Down with tyranny!"

Mendeleyev, who had a stack of books under his arm and was on his way to the library, found himself wedged between the surging crowd of demonstrators and an exodus of other students from the afternoon classes. Unwilling to push and shove, he stayed where he was.

"My friends,"—the voice of the speaker was clear and impassioned—"My friends, it was two years ago, on April 22, 1849, that Feodor Dostoevsky was arrested for no other crime than reading aloud at a friend's house a letter that had been handed to him. Today, branded, in fetters, with head shaven, Russia's great novelist carries bricks and cuts alabaster at the Siberian prison of Omsk, laboring in temperatures of forty degrees below zero. He is ill, mistreated . . . but not forgotten . . ."

The air was mild, but Mendeleyev shivered. He shared the indignation of all Russia at Dostoevsky's fate. A few days ago he had received a letter from Olga, describing the arrival of the novelist's convoy at Tobolsk on their way to Omsk. She was writing for Bassargin, who never wrote, knowing that a letter from a Decembrist would be sufficient to put Mendeleyev under suspicion. The women of Tobolsk,

Olga told him, had bribed the officials to let them send gifts of food and wine to Dostoevsky and his comrades. It was the least they could do. Her letter had evoked a sense of helpless anger in him which now, hearing the speaker, returned to him.

"Dmitri Ivanovitch!" A fellow classmate, whom he knew only slightly, was at his side. "I did not expect to see you here. There is a meeting tonight. About Dostoevsky. Would you like to come?"

Mendeleyev hesitated, sorely tempted. Then he shook his head. "I am sorry. I have no time."

"Later then," said the student, as the shifting crowd separated them.

"Since coming to the throne, the Tsar Nicholas I has carried on a campaign of oppression," the speaker was saying. "Nikolai Gogol . . . because he criticized serfdom in *Dead Souls* . . . forced to flee to Rome where he died an exile. Turgenev silenced because of his obituary of Gogol . . . The Tsar has more censors than there are books published. . . . They delete the phrase 'forces of nature' from our physics books and 'free currents of air' from the cookbooks, and they even scrutinize works of music, searching for a liberal crescendo or a radical lentissimo. . . ."

There was an outburst of laughter in the audience, but the speaker raised his hand for silence, and continued.

"Philosophy, a 'dangerous subject,' is banished from the university. In the classics all reference to 'the free democracy of Athens' is barred. The secret police are no less numerous than the censors. Men are judged insane for uttering opinions in disagreement with officialdom, and are torn from their families to rot in dungeons. The road to Siberia runs with the blood of those who spoke out for justice. . . . What is to be done?" His voice thundered these last five words.

"Police!"

The warning rippled through the audience. With the skill of practice, the demonstrators melted away. The students who, like Mendeleyev, were present by accident, retreated hastily into the university building. He watched, petrified, as a group of uniformed guards rushed up and seized several stragglers, dragging them away. Then with a bound he followed the others up the university steps.

In the safety of the dim halls, Mendeleyev stood panting and shaken. Expulsion was the least penalty for attending a demonstration. Should that happen, his mother's tears of disappointment would flow even from her grave. "Work and not words." If he were to serve Russia, which he fervently wished to do, it must not be by shouting in the streets.

At seventeen he had changed vastly from the schoolboy who had childishly pelted rocks at his Latin grammar. Sorrow and loneliness had welded his determination to achieve something worthwhile. His classes and his studies occupied his days and nights and weekends. He slept little and often forgot to report for meals.

Voskresensky, his chemistry professor, advised him to slow down. "You cannot expect to learn everything all at once."

Mendeleyev agreed—but went right on as before. There was no doubt in his mind now that chemistry was to be his vocation. In Voskresensky's classes, as he passed each threshold of the "fortress of knowledge," he realized how complicated was his chosen subject, how much there was to learn, how much was still unknown about the nature of matter.

Voskresensky based his instruction on the teachings of a great Swedish chemist, John Jacob Berzelius, who had identified a number of new elements and who was even better known for his convenient system of using the first one or two letters of the Latin names of the elements in chemical formulas. For instance: O for oxygen, H for hydrogen, Au for gold (aurum), Fe for iron (ferum). Before Berzelius, the elements had been represented by picture symbols—a new moon for silver, a looking glass for copper, the lance and shield of Mars for iron. To write down the simplest formula by these picture symbols was the work of a draftsman, and to add to the confusion not all chemists had used the same symbols. As far back as 1817 Berzelius had pioneered in establishing accurate relative atomic weights of the elements.

In Voskresensky's classes, Mendeleyev heard of modern chemists of French, German, English and other nationalities whose theories were being debated widely in European scientific circles. Because of the language barrier, reports of these foreign scientists came slowly to Russia. Mendeleyev set to work to master French and German so he could read their scientific journals. He learned a little English but never became proficient in it.

Professor Zinin, his first acquaintance in St. Petersburg, continued to take an interest in him. On Monday evenings, Mendeleyev, with other chemistry students from the Pedagogical Institute as well as the university and the Academy of Medicine, met in Zinin's laboratory for informal discussions. They considered themselves a sort of Chemistry Club.

Here Mendeleyev made a few friends of his own age, among them a young medical student, Alexandre Porfirevich Borodin, son of a wealthy Georgian prince. Without jealousy, he noted that Borodin was Zinin's favorite; the professor treated the young Georgian as an adopted son. With a father's prerogative, he constantly scolded him for spending too much time playing chamber music with German friends.

"When you should be studying, you are thinking only of your music," he rebuked Borodin. "It is a mistake to chase two rabbits at one time."

For Mendeleyev there was only one rabbit—and that was science. For all his intensive work, at the end of his first year his grades were only fair. This was in truth not his fault. The institute gave freshmen courses only every other year. Mendeleyev had enrolled in the fall of 1850, which was not a freshman year, and consequently had to start with the sophomores. Though he had failed in none, he insisted on repeating some of his courses. By the end of the second year he had more than caught up with the others.

His summer vacations were merely extensions of his university work. He spent them in mineralogical and botanical field trips conducted by his professors. His interest in mineralogy was reflected in his first two scientific papers. *The Analysis of Finnish Allanite* was published by the St. Petersburg Mineralogical Society, an honor given to no other undergraduate. He followed this with another paper on Finnish minerals, which later was also published by the Mineralogical Society.

In the middle of his third year he became seriously ill with throat hemorrhages and had to spend weeks in the institute hospital. Stubbornly, he insisted on studying, even in his sick bed, relying on his fellow students to bring him his books and assignments. Voskresensky came periodically and gave him private instruction. Because of this prolonged illness, the school authorities proposed a transfer to the University of Kiev, where the climate was warmer and drier. He refused. He was learning too much and too well to risk a change. He returned to his classes before the doctor pronounced him cured, and ill-health plagued him for the rest of his student days. So far as possible, he ignored it.

In his fourth year at the university, his chemistry laboratory project was the study of the crystalline structure of natural minerals, an interest that had originated after the glass factory fire, when he noticed that the molten glass, on hardening, formed into innumerable tiny crystals. Now he grew his crystals in bottles containing various solutions, hovering over them as lovingly as a gardener.

In 1821, the German chemist Eilhard Mitscherlich had discovered that in crystallized compounds certain elements can replace each other without any apparent change in crystalline form. (For instance, the phosphates of ammonium and potassium have crystalline shapes similar to the arsenates of ammonium and potassium.) Mitscherlich called this phenomenon *isomorphism.* Mendeleyev repeated Mitscherlich's experiments and devised new ones of his own. From his observations he wrote his diploma thesis, a 234-page manuscript titled *Isomorphism in Connection with Other Relations Between Crystalline Forms and Chemical Constitutions.*

If phosphates and arsenates were interchangeable in crystals, was there not some definite relationship between the elements phosphorus and arsenic? Or between other elements that were similarly interchangeable? Mendeleyev puzzled over this, realizing that not he, nor likely anybody else, knew enough to find an answer. Nonetheless he began to keep notebooks, in which he jotted down all known facts about each of the elements. It was no more than a reference file for a future work, about which his ideas were still extremely hazy.

That winter of 1854–55, while Mendeleyev was absorbed in preparing his thesis, thousands of Russian soldiers were dying in the defense of Sevastopol, Russia's naval base on the tip of the Crimea. Nicholas I was unwilling to believe that French, Turkish and English troops were on Russian soil, and that the almost endless stream of recruits from all over his vast country was unable to dislodge them. He died on March 2, 1855, some said of a broken heart because of the Crimean failure.

His son, Alexander II, came to the throne, bringing hope to the serfs and their supporters. The new Tsar was known to have a kind heart. As heir-apparent, he had visited Western Siberia, talked with some of the political exiles, and was so stirred by their plight that he had begged his father to reduce their sentences. Though his plea was ignored by Nicholas, the gesture had made him many friends among the poor and oppressed.

In the early summer of 1855, Dmitri Ivanovitch Mendeleyev graduated from the Pedagogical Institute first in his class. His brilliant work on isomorphism was in part responsible. As the foremost student, he was handed a gold medal at the graduation ceremony, though, in accordance with custom, the examiners praised not him, but his chemistry professor, Voskresensky, for having created such a gifted pupil. Professor Zinin, who had followed Mendeleyev's work closely, commented: "He's like some sort of an elusive compound, something rare defying analysis."

While professors and examiners alike prophesied a brilliant future for him, they were deeply worried. The lad from Tobolsk, Siberia, had grown taller, but he was pale, thin as a broomstick, and coughed as often as he spoke. Frequently he coughed blood.

He went to see his physician, Dr. Zdekauer, at the Institute hospital. "I want to know what is the matter with me," he blurted out.

"You don't guess?" the doctor stalled.

"My father and two sisters died of tuberculosis. I presume that is my trouble."

Zdekauer nodded soberly.

"How long do I have?"

"Six months, perhaps," the doctor said. "That is, if you are careful."

He refused to let the doctor's verdict change his way of life. The Institute had become his home, the only one he knew, and he stayed on to study for his Master of Science degree. But day by day his health worsened.

Professor Voskresensky summoned him to his office.

"There are two high school teaching posts vacant unexpectedly," he told him. "They are in Simferopol in the Crimea and Odessa on the Black Sea, both southern cities bathed in sunlight. As a gold medalist, you can have your choice. My recommendation is Odessa. It has an excellent library, where you can find all the books you need to prepare for your degree."

"Are you ordering me to leave, Professor?" Mendeleyev asked.

"The Institute authorities think it is necessary. The fog of St. Petersburg is killing you, Dmitri Ivanovitch."

"Nonsense," he scoffed. "I don't think . . ."

Whatever he was going to say was blocked by a paroxysm of coughing, more violent than any that had preceded it. Recovering, he shrugged his shoulders.

"Odessa, did you say? Very well, I'll go to Odessa."

He filled out the necessary papers of application, but unfortunately there was a mix-up in the Ministry of Education, and a certain Yankievich was appointed to the Odessa post. Voskresensky protested vainly. Once the Ministry of

Education made a mistake, there was no way of undoing it. Mendeleyev had to be content with the lesser post at Simferopol in the Crimea. He left St. Petersburg on August 25, 1855.

4

SIX MONTHS TO LIVE

SOUTH OF THE STEPPES OF THE UKRAINE, THE CRIMEAN PENIN-
sula is an odd-shaped jewel dangling from a narrow thread
of land into the inky waters of the Black Sea. Simferopol,
in the southern center of the peninsula, protected from
off-coast winds by the range of Yalta Mountains, was a
lovely town set in a forest of olive and laurel trees and
surrounded with orchards and vineyards. When Mendeleyev
arrived, the worst of the summer heat was past. The sun's
rays were warm and friendly but not blistering. After the
perpetual dampness of St. Petersburg, it was paradise.

He reported to the officials of his high school, who welcomed him cordially, assigned him a room within the school
and told him to enjoy himself. Classes had not yet begun.

He could have prepared his curriculum, but he was not
in the mood. Day after day he wandered aimlessly out into
the country. For hours he stretched on his back in some
green meadow watching the flight of the butterflies, turning over to study the march of tiny energetic insects.
On his way back to town, he usually stopped at some
peasant's hut, chatting with his hosts about the state of
their crops and drinking the warm milk and munching on
the fresh bread and piles of purple grapes they set before
him. He had not been so indolent since he could remember.

48

It did him good. He coughed less and felt his strength returning.

For this brief idyllic period, he refused to think of his illness. He tried not to think of anything but the harmony of nature, the crystal blue of the sky, the perfection of the bright-colored autumn flowers, the soft purple shades of twilight and the majesty of the star-filled nights. But he could not for long shut out the Crimean War.

On September 8, 1855, the cannons at Sevastopol, fifty miles away, stopped roaring. The Russian commander, Prince Michael Gortchakoff, had evacuated the great naval base after a siege of eleven months. When the Allies triumphantly marched in they found only ruins and rubble. From St. Petersburg, Alexander II, in the tradition of his father, ordered Gortchakoff to keep fighting; not until March 30 of the following year did the Treaty of Paris bring peace.

Simferopol became a military base, under martial law, filled with soldiers. There were mounted Cossacks, their muskets at their sides, slant-eyed Tartars in colored jackets, serfs who had fled their masters and joined up in the hope of purchasing their freedom. From the abandoned naval base came a stream of refugees—the walking wounded, gray-faced and weary; gaunt half-starved horses with their burdens of men barely able to sit upright; camel-drawn telegas piled high with those almost past caring whether they lived or died. The hospital was overflowing.

Already the futile war had cost 300,000 lives, Allied and Russian, mostly through disease, exposure and privation. It had been rife with military blunders, among them that described in Tennyson's "The Charge of the Light Brigade": "Theirs not to reason why; Theirs but to do and die; Into the Valley of Death, Rode the six hundred." On the Russian side, the terrible days of the siege were immortalized in

Sketches of Sevastopol, written by a young officer called Leo Tolstoy. The courage of the common soldiers on both sides was legendary. There was one outstanding heroine, the British nurse Florence Nightingale.

Because of the war, the Simferopol high school did not open. Mendeleyev received the salary due him and the apologies of the town for the events beyond their control. Under the influx of the military, practically all provisions vanished from the shops. Obviously it was useless for him to stay longer. Rather than return to St. Petersburg, he decided to try his luck in Odessa. Though the post he had wanted was held by another, it seemed likely there might be other positions open in this large seaport city.

Winter was already hovering near when, on October 30, he left Simferopol. "I set out," he wrote his brother Paul, "wearing a short fur coat that offered poor protection against the night frosts, bearskin boots, and a tall fur hat. I drove from the Crimea with a month's salary in my pocket and hope in my heart." He had begun to grow a beard, and his hair, no longer short and neatly parted in the fashion of European St. Petersburg, hung down around his ears like that of any Russian peasant.

His eccentric appearance was not held against him in cosmopolitan Odessa, a city of artists, intellectuals, retired military officers, merchants and nobility, and vacationers come to enjoy the splendid beaches. Except for a brief naval skirmish at the beginning of hostilities, the war had left no traces here. People were hospitable and helpful to the young graduate student from St. Petersburg. Mendeleyev soon found a post teaching physics and mathematics at the Richelieu high school.

He had neglected to report to the hospital at Simferopol, because he knew the staff was overworked with war casual-

ties, and with all the suffering around him, the state of his
own health seemed unimportant. An urgent message from
Dr. Zdekauer, who had just learned his whereabouts in
Odessa, instructed him to go at once to Dr. Nicolai Ivanovitch Pirogov, a former physician at the Pedagogical Institute.

With no further excuse for delay, Mendeleyev called
on Dr. Pirogov.

"So you are the gold medalist from the institute of whom
Zdekauer wrote me?" The Odessa physician was a black-
bearded genial giant with penetrating deep blue eyes, who
seemed in a flash to understand Mendeleyev's character,
his ambitions and his apprehensions. "They tell me you have
been ill. A serious mistake to tax yourself beyond your
endurance. Russia needs healthy scientists, not sick ones.
Come inside and we'll take a look at you."

His examination was thorough and professional. When
it was over, his eyes were twinkling. "You can write Zdekauer
that I prophesy you will outlive us both," he told Mendeleyev.
"You do not have tuberculosis and have never had it." His
trouble, Pirogov went on to say, was caused by a valvular
defect, a functional condition of the heart. Because of this,
he had coughed blood and might do so in the future, but
he had nothing to fear. There was no reason why he should
not live to a very old age.

The good news sent Mendeleyev racing and reeling down
the streets. He stopped, breathless, beneath the bronze
statue of the Duc de Richelieu, Odessa's former governor,
which stood majestically at the top of the two-hundred wide
granite steps leading down to the harbor.

"Good-day, Monsieur le Duc," said Mendeleyev with a
mock bow. "Life is wonderful!" He shouted the same words
Bassargin had used on another joyous occasion. "*Akh*, Mon-

sieur le Duc, how wonderful is life." Throwing back his head, he roared with laughter.

Death had taken a long look at him and passed him by. Now he was free to do the things he wanted to do, without that solemn specter hanging over his shoulder, telling him incessantly that he had no time. He felt capable of conquering the world.

A few passers-by turned and stared tolerantly at him. Obviously, they reasoned, the big blond noisy young man was a sailor who had had too much to drink.

The next day he was ready for the wonderful life that had been given back to him.

Teaching physics and mathematics to the students of Richelieu high school took only a portion of his time. He made friends, enjoyed himself at social gatherings, picnics and beach parties. Best of all, through the influence of Dr. Pirogov, "his savior" as he henceforth called him, he was granted permission to use the library and laboratory of Novorossisk University, the finest institute of learning in southern Russia.

Soon he was deep in research—on the expansion of elements under heat, and on specific volumes, the latter having to do with the ratio of the volume of one substance to the volume of the same weight of another substance, particularly in regard to elements that could be substituted for each other in certain compounds. "Specific Volumes" became the subject for his Master of Science thesis, and he worked on it all winter and spring. By May of 1856, at the end of his first year of teaching, he had completed the first draft of the thesis, a manuscript of 224 pages.

That month he left hospitable Odessa to return to St. Petersburg. His colleagues gasped, hardly able to believe that this husky young Viking with the booming voice and the splendid blond beard was the same emaciated youth who had been given just six months to live. He passed his preliminary examinations with ease, receiving the highest mark of all who took them.

By the end of the summer his thesis, "Specific Volumes," was revised and corrected. As a result, the Council of St. Petersburg University unanimously voted to confer on him —at the age of twenty-two—the degree of Master of Physics and Chemistry. The event was recorded in a dry comment:

"On Sunday, September 9, at 1:00 P.M., in the St. Petersburg University, D. Mendeleyev, a former pupil of the Pedagogical Institute, presented his thesis on specific volumes and related subjects. . . . The candidate's own experiments and the conclusions he drew from them were received with general approval. They offered the possibility of distinguishing by volume in the solid state the phenomenon of substitution from the phenomenon of combination and pointed the way to the natural classification of chemical combinations on the basis of their specific volumes."

"Natural classification of chemical combinations." The phrase was significant. In this work, as in that on isomorphism, Mendeleyev had been impressed by similar properties in elements superficially quite different. He still did not know why this was so, but he did not forget about it.

Six weeks later he had another scientific paper to present to the university, *The Structure of Siliceous Combinations*. This won him an appointment as lecturer at St. Petersburg University. He could now instruct undergraduates in theoretical and organic chemistry, though not as a full professor. At the same time he was elected Secretary of the University Department of Chemistry, a fine title which meant merely that he was responsible for the tedious administrative details of the department.

"Work and not words." Besides his teaching and secretarial duties, he spent long hours in the laboratory and at his desk, writing and reading foreign journals. To his colleagues, it seemed as though he had a magic gift for stretching a twenty-four-hour day into twice its normal length. Between 1856 and 1858 he published some fifteen papers and articles.

The Ministry of Education, impressed by his talent for writing about science clearly and logically, appointed him to take charge of their department of scientific information. For the Ministry *Journal* he wrote a series of articles on subjects of value to manufacturers. One was "New Dye Stuffs." Another, "Liquid Glass or Glazes and the Methods of Supplying Them." Their theme was that the advance of production and the advance of science were interrelated. "The effort to use the abstract theories of science in real life is a notable feature of our times," he wrote.

In the midst of his multitudinous duties, he fell in love, or thought he did. Sophia Markovna Kash was just sixteen, fragile and dainty. They became engaged, but later her father insisted she break the engagement because of her extreme youth. When it was over, he was actually relieved. He did not yet feel ready for marriage.

It was at about this time that Alexander II, true to his early promise, permitted the Decembrists to return from their Siberian exile. Among them came Olga and Bassargin, the latter exhausted and ill but still with an unconquerable spirit. Though they did not live near Mendeleyev, he managed to see them from time to time and renewed the former bonds of affection.

The Tsar had frequently expressed sympathy with the serfs, and in March of 1856 he told his nobility that it was "better to abolish serfdom from the top than to wait until it began to be abolished from the bottom." There the matter rested. Impatient students distributed circulars demanding action, but they were arrested and thown in prison. Conditions were no different from those during the reign of Nicholas I.

The former atmosphere of suspicion returned. At St. Petersburg University, in 1858, a student was arrested for having in his possesion an English copy of Emerson's *Self-Reliance*. The professor who had loaned it to him went to the police and told them he was the owner of this "incendiary" volume. Only then was the youth released.

"Stupidity," muttered Mendeleyev, referring to the government attitude. "Foolish and foolhardy," he said more gently of the students who thought they could reform the world.

His own personal grievance at the time was the lack of proper laboratory facilities and equipment. The university laboratory consisted of two tiny rooms with stone floors, so poorly ventilated that researchers had to stop in the middle of an experiment and dash out for a breath of fresh air. The laboratory apparatus was unworthy of the name. There was not a test tube to be had in the shops of St. Petersburg. Mendeleyev and his assistants made their own from rubber.

Mendeleyev, who had found it much better at Odessa, fumed and stormed, wrote articles about the shortsightedness of leaving scientists without the tools of their trade, pressed the university authorities and the Ministry of Education for additional funds. So far his efforts had failed to produce results.

One evening in January of 1859, Professor Zinin stopped in at the laboratory where Mendeleyev was working late, groaning and mumbling to himself as he handled his pipettes and balances.

Zinin watched him a few moments unobserved. "Do you always swear when you work, Dmitri Ivanovitch?" he asked at last.

Mendeleyev looked up with a start. "Can you blame me?" he grumbled. "I've done the same experiment sixteen times and had sixteen different results. Nothing goes properly in this cursed laboratory."

Zinin tugged at his mustaches. "When I was at the University of Kiev, there was a saying among the chemists that the worse the laboratory, the better the research done in it."

Mendeleyev was not amused. "That sounds very pretty but you know as well as I do there's no truth in it," he snorted. "When will Russia learn to spend at least a small per cent of the money on science which now goes to her armies—or her secret police?"

"How would you like to leave all this?" Zinin asked unexpectedly.

Briefly it flashed through Mendeleyev's mind that he was being dismissed, that perhaps his work had not been good enough, or that his outspokenness had displeased the Ministry of Education. He sat down heavily.

"Voskresensky and I have been discussing you with the University Council," Zinin was saying. "We told them that when the time comes you are the obvious candidate to replace one of us in a professorial chair of chemistry. To prepare for this eventuality under the handicaps you have here is well-nigh impossible. We want you to have the best opportunities available. The university has agreed to send you to Germany for two years' work, 'for the improvement of your scientific knowledge,' with all expenses paid. What do you think of that?"

Mendeleyev relaxed. "You know very well I would like it, Professor. If I have a choice, I would suggest Heidelberg. Kirchhoff and Bunsen are doing some interesting work there on spectrum analysis. When do I leave?"

"At the end of the spring term," Zinin said, again stroking his long mustaches. "Your allowance will be moderate but should be enough for your needs, which I know are not excessive."

Three and a half years had passed since he had gone to Simferopol, under a death sentence. In that time his health had been restored, he had his master's degree and had written a string of papers, which had given him a reputation within the confines of Russia. Now he was off to broaden his horizons.

5

HEIDELBERG

By April of 1859, Mendeleyev was in Paris. Voskresensky, long an admirer of French science, had insisted he make this his first stop. That it was spring and the chestnut trees were in bloom in this city of culture and tradition registered but vaguely with the dedicated young scientist. He spent his time between his lodgings and the laboratory of the physicist-chemist Henri Regnault, who had granted him the freedom of his laboratory.

Regnault was investigating the density and specific heats of gases and the compressibility and dilation of fluids. Mendeleyev was deeply impressed at the precision with which the Frenchman conducted his experiments. In spite of language handicaps, he acquired new techniques and improved his own skills during the brief period of his stay.

Heidelberg came next. This famous university town, with its medieval and Renaissance buildings and almost legendary castle, was a mecca for students from all over Europe. A number of them were Russian. It came as a surprise to Mendeleyev to hear his own language spoken in the halls and grounds of the University of Heidelberg, not only by male students but by young women as well.

Some of these Russian girls were dressed fashionably in long velvet dresses and chignons. Others, in the style of modern "emancipated women," wore their hair cut short, round and saucy Garibaldi caps on their heads and glasses on their noses. They had come abroad to get the education still forbidden to them at home. Some took courses in history and even law. To Mendeleyev's relief, they had not invaded the science department, which was still a man's domain.

The University of Heidelberg had a number of fine scientists on its faculty, the most famous perhaps, Robert Wilhelm Bunsen, an investigator of first rank. He had done original research on organic arsenic compounds and exact methods of gas analysis. Even better known was the laboratory apparatus he had invented—the Bunsen battery, the grease-spot photometer, the absorptiometer, the actinometer and, of course, his celebrated Bunsen burner, a hollow cylindrical tube fitting vertically around a flame, with an opening at the base to admit air, which produced a smokeless nonluminous flame of high temperature.

His latest invention, done in collaboration with another Heidelberg professor, Gustav Robert Kirchhoff, was a spectroscope, by which, according to scientific journals, the spectra of certain elements could be distinguished. It was this which had drawn Mendeleyev to Heidelberg. On his arrival he signed up for Bunsen's lecture courses and then reported to him personally.

"You are Mendeleyev, the Russian chemist, and you want to work in my laboratory? Very good." Dr. Bunsen was a clean-shaven gray-haired man, with regular features and tight lips. "You will find that here every experiment is conducted with flawless precision. We do not allow sloppy methods."

There was nothing unkind in the German professor's greeting, but Mendeleyev suspected a touch of patronage, as if, to Bunsen, "Russian chemist" and "sloppy methods" were synonymous. He was relieved when Bunsen called in his associate, Gustav Kirchhoff, and asked him to show their visiting researcher around the laboratory.

Kirchhoff, a man in his midthirties with a full brown beard and a warm, eager, modest manner, was as friendly as Bunsen was formal. He led Mendeleyev through the laboratory, introduced him to the other student-researchers, showed him their equipment, including the marvelous Bunsen burner, and finally displayed the spectroscope, his special pride and joy. It was, actually, surprisingly simple— a prism attached to a long tube with a slit at the bottom.

"I would like to know the principle of the thing," Mendeleyev said in his faulty German.

Delighted, Kirchhoff had him sit down.

"You may know," he spoke slowly out of courtesy to the foreigner, "that when the white light of the sun strikes a prism, the light is bent, dividing into a continuous band of rainbow colors. Violet bends the most and red the least. Orange, yellow, green, blue and indigo bend at angles between violet and red. Now you will see what happens when the flame of potassium strikes the prism."

As he prepared to burn the sample, Mendeleyev was transported back into the past, watching the old chemist at the Aremziansk glass factory. He followed Kirchhoff's movements with the same absorption.

"So you see," Kirchhoff was saying, "when the purple flame of potassium reaches the prism, it divides into red and blue beams and other colors. A sodium flame produces two yellow beams, close together. Every element, we have reason to believe, when heated to incandescence, has its distinctive spectrum."

"How very useful!" Mendeleyev exclaimed, genuinely excited. "How very useful to detect and identify new elements, the existence of which no one has suspected."

"Yes," said Kirchhoff, "that is exactly what we are working on. Nor is that all. By means of the spectroscope, we are now studying the spectrum of the sun. It is thus possible to establish that the sun's atmosphere contains some of the same elements that we have here on earth. Eventually, we may prove that this is also true of the stars. My present project has to do with the Fraunhofer lines. You remember that the German optician Fraunhofer mapped out the dark lines in the solar spectrum about thirty years ago, though he could give no reason for them. It is my theory that the glowing vapors of the sun absorb the same radiation they emit—hence the dark lines. . . ."

As Kirchhoff chatted on about his work, Mendeleyev listened rapturously. This was the kind of talk he liked best. Science, he had always felt, was not just a matter of test tubes and pipettes. It stretched out to encompass the entire universe. How lucky he was to be in Heidelberg!

With Kirchhoff's able tutoring, he mastered the technique of the spectroscope in the next weeks. There were, however, disadvantages to working in this laboratory. One was that he was assigned to share a table with a researcher who was working on sulfur compounds. The noxious fumes kept Mendeleyev coughing, threatening him with a relapse of his old ailment.

Just as serious was an undercurrent of dissension between him and Bunsen. As a researcher in his laboratory, he was expected to follow to the letter the assignments Bunsen gave him. He was accustomed to independence, to pursuing his own ideas and theories. To proceed in the paths of experimentation set by another was torture for him. One day he walked out and did not return. Though he would continue to attend the lectures of Bunsen and Kirchhoff, he had made up his mind to have his own laboratory.

In Heidelberg, unlike St. Petersburg, one could buy modern laboratory equipment. He cut down on food and used the money he saved to fit his laboratory in one of the rooms in his lodgings. A master glass blower made him special thermometers and pycnometers (instruments for determining the specific gravity of liquids) to his specifications. He built some of his apparatus himself.

All these preparations were for a new piece of research— the investigation of capillarity, the phenomenon by which the surface of a liquid at the edges of its container is either higher or lower than the rest. (A simple example: the surface of water in a glass jar is slightly higher where water and glass meet. In mercury, on the other hand, the surface is slightly lower at the edges.) Mendeleyev deduced that the reason for capillarity had to do with the cohesive forces between the molecules of the liquid. When it was heated, the "cohesive force" lessened.

"When cohesion reaches zero," he wrote, "the liquid should become . . . a body possessing no cohesion—a gas . . ."

He called the temperature at which a liquid vaporized into a gas the "absolute temperature" or "absolute boiling point." If every liquid could be heated to its "absolute temperature," it followed that every gas could be cooled to its "absolute temperature."

While scientists at this time had solidified certain gases under high pressure, they had been unable to solidify other gases, such as nitrogen, oxygen and hydrogen. It was generally held that there were two types of gases, those which could be condensed into liquids and those which could not be. Mendeleyev refused to accept the "two types of gas" theory.

"The non-liquefaction of well-known gases, such as nitrogen, oxygen and hydrogen," he wrote in 1860, "is probably due to the fact that experiments were conducted at temperatures above the absolute boiling point. The more the gases selected for liquefaction are cooled, the greater our hopes of being able to liquefy them."

Nine years later, the Irish chemist Thomas Andrews would give the name of "critical temperatures" to what Mendeleyev had called "absolute temperatures" and would be generally credited as the originator of the theory, though Mendeleyev was his predecessor. Eventually researchers would succeed in cooling all gases to their "critical temperatures."

By tradition, student life in nineteenth-century Heidelberg was a composite of duels, drinking bouts, songs and romance. For Mendeleyev, as single-minded now as he had been at the Pedagogical Institute, a good time meant meeting his fellow Russians at a tavern, coffeehouse or in their own lodgings for an evening of conversation.

"At Heidelberg, soon after my arrival," wrote Sechenov, one of these young Russians, "I found a great company of Russians. . . . Mendeleyev, of course, was the leader of our circle, if for no other reason than the fact that, though so young (younger than I), he was already a qualified chemist while we were still students."

The novelist Ivan Turgenev, another visitor, later wrote of "a young Russian chemist living in Heidelberg who was by all who knew him praised as an uncommon talent, so that they declared he will become one day a second Lavoisier." Only Mendeleyev could have fitted this description.

Late the first winter an old friend of Mendeleyev's arrived, Alexandre Borodin, the medical student whom Professor Zinin had warned against "chasing two rabbits at the same time." The warning had gone unheeded; while chemistry was his vocation, music was still his hobby. When spring came, he and Mendeleyev decided to make a trip to Italy together for their vacation.

They took only one knapsack for the two of them, and wore artists' blouses on the theory that since Italians were sympathetic to artists, the innkeepers would reduce their fees. When their linen became soiled they gave it away and bought themselves a new supply. They visited Venice and Verona, which were still under Austrian rule, and Milan, which was part of the more liberal kingdom of Sardinia.

Between Verona and Milan they had a near misadventure. Their carriage was stopped and boarded by a contingent of mounted Austrian police, who scrutinized all the passengers in turn. They ignored the tall and blond-bearded Mendeleyev, but came to a halt before Borodin, who had the dark hair and eyes of his Georgian ancestors. The police were looking for an escaped Italian prisoner and apparently Borodin matched the description.

Vainly Borodin offered papers to prove his identity, while Mendeleyev protested volubly in all the languages he knew. The Austrians either did not or would not understand. They searched them both and ransacked their knapsack. Only then were they convinced that the two young men really were both peaceful Russian students on a holiday. After a profuse apology, they rode off in a swirl of dust.

As the carriage drove on toward Milan, there was an

almost ominous silence among the other passengers. Borodin and Mendeleyev were puzzled. Everyone had been talkative enough before the incident of the police. The silence lasted until they crossed the Austrian border into Sardinia. At once their traveling companions jumped from their seats, shouted "Evvivia!" and began singing at the top of their voices.

The two bewildered Russians found themselves the focus of attention. Women, and men too, embraced them and showered them with delicacies from their lunchbaskets. In the midst of the hubbub, a swarthy young man, with tears streaming down his cheeks, thanked them for saving him from the clutches of the Austrian swine! It turned out that he was the escaped prisoner the police had been seeking. Because of Borodin's dark Latin good looks, they had not noticed him.

That fall, Borodin and Mendeleyev took another holiday to Genoa and Rome. After that Mendeleyev saw little of his friend. Borodin had become enamored of a young Russian girl, Catherine Protopopova, who was in Heidelberg for her health. She was an excellent pianist, and her fine renditions of Chopin and Schumann were certainly part of her attraction to Borodin. They were married on their return to Russia. Mendeleyev remained convinced that marriage was a fine thing for his friends but that it had no part in his way of life.

In December, 1860, the first International Congress of Chemists was held in Karlsruhe. Russia was represented by Mendeleyev, Borodin and Nicolai Zinin, their former professor. Zinin and Mendeleyev were both on the committee that drafted the Congress resolutions.

At the Congress, chemists of different nationalities had a chance to exchange ideas and discuss their own work. Its main purpose was to try to establish uniformity of scientific concepts and terminology, where previously, in Mendeleyev's words, "turbid confusion reigned."

Up until this time scientists often used the words "atoms" and "molecules" interchangeably. Some called molecules "compound atoms," as John Dalton had done. Some took their cue from Amedeo Avogadro, Dalton's Italian successor, and called atoms "elementary molecules."

In 1811 Avogadro had formulated his "law of gases"—that under the same conditions of temperature and pressure equal volumes of different gases contain equal numbers of molecules. This momentous discovery had paved the way to establishing accurate relative atomic weights of the elements. Thus, if two identical containers were filled, one with hydrogen and the other with oxygen, Avogadro found that the oxygen weighed about sixteen times as much as the hydrogen, and judged accordingly that the atomic weight of oxygen was about sixteen times that of hydrogen.

But by the time of the Congress of Karlsruhe, Avogadro's law of gases had fallen into neglect. There was some doubt as to whether the principle behind it was valid for all branches of chemistry. Some scientists, for instance, insisted that there were two quite different chemistries—one for organic substances and one for inorganic substances.

The divergent opinions expressed at the Congress were, in fact, enough to bewilder anyone. To Voskresensky, in St. Petersburg, Mendeleyev wrote: "Some wanted to define the particles [atoms or molecules] of each substance by acknowledging only the chemical properties, i.e., reactions; others thought it necessary to recognize only the physical characteristics; and a third declared both aspects to be identical."

Toward the end of the sessions, an Italian professor, Stanislao Cannizarro, rose to his feet to say that he believed there should be one set of atomic weights for all branches of chemistry, organic or inorganic. This sounded reasonable to Mendeleyev, but others objected and the meeting ended on this discordant note, with nothing resolved but a general agreement that each chemist should continue to use his own system. Mendeleyev was not alone in feeling dissatisfied.

Following the meeting, Cannizarro had his assistant distribute a pamphlet he had written with the formidable title, *A Course of Chemical Philosophy Given in the Royal University of Genoa.* It was a summary of the lectures this farsighted Italian chemist was giving to his students in Genoa. In it he reiterated that there was but "one science of chemistry and one set of atomic weights." He emphasized the importance of Avogadro's law of gases in establishing molecular and atomic weights. And he clearly defined an atom as the smallest unit of an element, and a molecule as the smallest unit of a compound.

Mendeleyev read Cannizarro's pamphlet with delight. So did many others. A German scientist, Lothar Meyer, said that after studying it, "the scales fell from my eyes, doubts vanished, and the feeling of calm certainty came in their place." Because of Cannizarro, the Karlsruhe Congress of 1860 would be a milestone in chemical history. For Mendeleyev it was the high point of his stay abroad. Soon afterward, in February 1861, he was summoned back to St. Petersburg to give a course of lectures on organic chemistry.

Through various publications in French and German scientific journals, his name was beginning to be known outside of Russia. He was only twenty-seven and his career had barely begun.

6

WORK AND MARRIAGE

No HINT OF SPRING HAD REACHED ST. PETERSBURG WHEN
Mendeleyev's coach arrived on a Sunday morning in March
of 1861. White mists, barely pierced by a pale sun, hung
low over the canals, and the wrought-iron bridges seemed to
float unsupported in space. As the coach rumbled down the
empty cobblestoned streets, the familiar vista of colorful
steep-roofed mansions, domed and gleaming cathedrals,
and pleasant open squares unfolded.

Mendeleyev felt his heart turn over. Paris, Heidelberg,
Venice, Rome—all the beautiful foreign places he had seen
—paled before the riotous splendor of Peter the Great's
city built on the swamps. The fog was lifting when they
reached the Winter Palace on the Neva, a long quarter mile
of pillars, porticos and ornately decorated windows. With
surprise he noted that in his absence it had been painted a
deep red, even more overwhelming than its former pistachio
green. The way was barred by a regiment of the King's
Guard, beyond which a huge crowd overflowed from the
plaza before the palace gate.

"You can't pass here," an officer snapped at them. "The
Emperor is speaking."

Grumbling, the driver pulled to a halt. Curious and excited, Mendeleyev pushed aside the heavy fur rug across

68

his knees and leaped from the coach to join the throng—
men and women, young and old, peasants, students and
well-dressed intellectuals. On the balcony above the palace
entrance stood the Tsar, Alexander II, a big man and im-
posing in his white and gold uniform. In the Russian speech
Mendeleyev had missed so deeply, his words rang clear
and resonant.

"The work was already begun in my father's day," he was
saying, "but he was unable to accomplish it in his lifetime.
With God's help, it fell to my lot to complete the task for
your good. Now, my children, go and thank God; pray for
the eternal repose of my father; prove yourself useful to
the fatherland."

As he finished, a chorus of cheers broke out. Old men
mumbled incoherently and wept. A peasant woman cried,
"How good he is—our Little Father!" The Emperor raised
his hand in blessing and vanished into the interior of the
palace.

"What work? What task? What did he mean?" Mendeleyev
asked a young man who stood near him.

The youth looked incredulously at the big blond-bearded
man in the foreign greatcoat. "You don't know? You are a
stranger, perhaps?"

"I have been away," Mendeleyev explained gently.

"The Tsar has freed the serfs," the youth said proudly.
"He signed the Manifesto of Freedom three weeks ago
today. All over Russia the bells are ringing."

"Thank God!" Mendeleyev cried. As he made his way
back to his coach, he felt the tears smarting in his own
eyes. At last justice had been done! How pleased Bassargin
must be!

But when he reached his university apartment, a note
was waiting for him from his sister, Olga, saying that Bas-

sargin was dead. "You know he had been very ill," she wrote. "Though he was in great pain he clung to life long enough to see the serfs liberated. Then he could die in peace."

Sobbing, Mendeleyev wandered through the cold and empty rooms of his apartment. His mother, Liza and now Bassargin—the three who had put all their faith in him—they were all gone now.

"*Akh,* how alone I am," he muttered.

As before, he turned to his work to efface the scars of grief.

In addition to his university lectures on organic chemistry, he taught chemistry at a military school and continued with his own research. So that Russian scientists could benefit from the work he had seen at Heidelberg, he translated several German works, adding his own analyses. He had become intensely interested in scientific agriculture, and for the Imperial Free Economics Society he analyzed soil from various sections of Russia.

In the meantime, the rejoicing caused by the Tsar's Manifesto of Freedom changed to discontent as the terms of the emancipation became known. Serfs were not to be freed immediately but only after two more years of bondage. The land they had been promised would not go to them directly but to their village commune, yet they would have to pay exorbitant taxes to reimburse the landowners. There were other compromises and restrictions.

In front of the University of St. Petersburg students resumed their demonstrations. More than four hundred were dragged away by the police; and on the Tsar's orders, all classes were closed and armed guards patrolled the buildings.

Politics! Always politics! While the ban lasted, Mendeleyev rigidly suppressed his own outrage at the injustice and concentrated on writing a textbook on organic chemistry, the first in Russian. The 502-page manuscript, *Organic Chemistry,* was completed in two months. It covered modern theories and discoveries, disparaged the "vitalists," who claimed that organic matter was not subject to the same chemical laws as inorganic matter, and called attention to scientific phenomena needing further investigation, for instance, isomerism.

Isomers are compounds with the same chemical composition which, for no reason anyone yet knew, were utterly unlike each other. A student of Mendeleyev's, A. M. Buterov, inspired by this book, investigated the mystery of isomerism and solved it: the reason for the difference in the compounds was that the arrangement of the atoms in the molecules was different. The whole vast field of molecular structure, so important in organic chemistry, was opened to further study.

Universities all over Russia welcomed *Organic Chemistry.* On the recommendation of Professor Zinin, the Russian Academy of Science awarded Mendeleyev their coveted Domidov Prize for this work.

In the spring of 1862, his sister Olga came to see him. She looked with horror at the cluttered rooms of his bachelor apartment.

"How can you live like this?" she scolded.

"What is wrong with the way I live?"

"Everything." Her despairing gesture encompassed the stacks of books and papers on the floor, on every chair and table. "Such confusion!"

"It is not confusing to me," he assured her. "I know where

everything is. A woman comes and cleans twice a week. What more do I need?"

"You need a home."

"But this is my home."

"You need a wife."

He grimaced. "No woman would ever put up with me."

"You are wrong, Dmitri," she said earnestly. "You remember Feozva Nitkitichna Leschev from Central Siberia? You met her once at our house and she liked you very much. I will arrange another meeting."

"You will do no such thing, Olga," he protested vigorously.

But his widowed sister was determined to get her friend and brother together, and in truth Mendeleyev did not really mind. Feozva was quiet, small, shy and admiring. That she was six years older than he did not bother him. At twenty-eight he no longer thought of himself as a young man. One evening he proposed to her, and she promptly accepted. He never was quite sure what made him do it.

Even during the early part of their engagement, he began to have qualms of doubt. "The more I know about my intended, the more I feel something is wrong," he wrote to Olga, who was away in Moscow. "I do not feel about her as a man should feel about a woman he is to marry."

Olga answered immediately: "You can't back out now, my brother. Remember what the poet Goethe said? 'There is no sin greater than to betray the trust of a maiden.' You are engaged. Your betrothal has been announced. Should you throw her out now, her life will be ruined."

Mendeleyev threw the letter aside indignantly. Let Goethe go to blazes! No one, not even the great German poet, was going to tell him how to run his life. How ironic that Olga, who had married Bassargin purely for love, should now insist that he go through with a loveless alliance! Yet in spite of his inner rebellion, he did nothing. He liked Feozva and had no desire to hurt her. Moreover, he disliked scenes.

They were married quietly, and for a time all went well. The university granted them a larger apartment, and they bought new furniture, drapes and dishes. He had his own combination study and laboratory. His books were stacked neatly on bookshelves. Feozva kept the samovar boiling and fetched him a cup of tea whenever he wanted it. His favorite dishes appeared on the dinner table. Getting settled took time from his work, but he could not deny the advantages of married life.

Within a few weeks he was back to his old routine, shutting himself in his study night after night, sometimes working through to dawn. Feozva chided him, playfully at first and then with a note of reproach. He tried to explain what he was doing.

"These are solutions," he told her, pointing to the bottles filled with liquid ranged behind his laboratory table. "There is considerable doubt whether a solution is a chemical combination or a mechanical mixture. That is, whether the atoms of the solvent and the solute—say salt and water, or sugar and water—unite to form molecules or whether they simply mix in equal proportion. Now I am working on alcohol and water solutions, and I find that when the alcohol and water are mixed in certain definite proportions, there is a contraction in the solution. My theory is that solutions are chemical compounds in a state of partial dissociation. . . ."

"You mean that you spend all this time mixing alcohol and water together?" she demanded, incredulously.

He made other attempts to take her with him on his

scientific explorations, but every time he failed dismally. Not only did she understand nothing, she was frankly bored. With horrifying clarity, he realized he could never share with her his life's work. He felt sorry for her, blamed himself for expecting too much of her, and in relief accepted an assignment from an industrialist named Kokorev to go to Baku on the Caspian Sea.

Kokorev owned a small oil refining company at Baku and wanted a scientific opinion of the possibilities of its development. Mendeleyev plunged with zest into this new field of endeavor. Baku was rich with oil. There was no doubt of that. The dark liquid seeping from the earth was so plentiful that people collected it in vats and poured it on the waters of the Caspian, setting fire to it for the pleasure of watching the towering flames. Yet commercial production was in its infancy and doing poorly.

A major handicap was that the land in which wells were sunk had to be leased from the government for a period of four years only, with no guarantee of renewal. Consequently operators tried to get as much oil as they could, as quickly as they could and at the least possible expense. They built shallow wells which produced more brine than oil. They solved their transportation problem by carting the oil to the harbor in leather sacks, wineskins or barrels, and in these containers it was loaded on ships.

On his return to St. Petersburg, Mendeleyev pressed for sharp reforms in government control and the abolishment of the four-year lease system. For the immediate future he advocated the building of oil tankers, and eventually a great pipeline to stretch the four hundred miles to the Black Sea, for better access to European markets.

Over the years he continued to act as consultant to the

oil industry, especially in the improvement of refining methods. This work he considered part of his obligation to Bassargin to use his scientific knowledge to enrich Russia and the Russian people.

This additional work did not interfere with his own research. In 1865 he was awarded the degree of Doctor of Chemistry on the basis of a 119-page thesis, *Combinations of Alcohols with Water.* At last he was entitled to an appointment as full professor. Even Feozvo admitted that mixing alcohol and water might not be as silly as it seemed.

The combined income from his writing, his consultation fees and his increased salary made him feel relatively wealthy. With a colleague he bought a half interest in a 365-acre estate on Boblovo Hill, seven hours by railroad from St. Petersburg. Henceforth their summer home was its big rambling farmhouse, set in a park of pines and oaks and spreading birches. In the fields, summer after summer, Mendeleyev experimented with scientific farming. Muzhiks came from miles around to watch in wonder this tall bearded young man from the city who raised rye with a yield three times that of their own.

"How is it done?" they asked humbly.

He showed them his barometer, his thermometer, the gauge that kept a record of how much rain fell, and the hygrometer that measured the humidity in the air. They nodded politely, but obviously did not see what these shining instruments had to do with the tilling of the soil. He told them that soil, to be productive, needed a number of substances—potassium, sodium, magnesium, carbon, nitrogen, phosphorus, iron . . .

Iron? The iron they used to shoe their horses? Plants fed on iron? If they did not burst out in laughter it was only because they knew that their neighbor, Dmitri Ivanovitch, was a professor. A learned man. He must know what he was talking about.

Feozva was certainly happier at Boblovo too. Busy with her household chores, she forgot the various ailments of which she had been complaining. Temporarily they were drawn closer together by their first-born, a fair-haired boy they named Volodya. Mendeleyev, who normally detested idling, always found time to romp with his son.

Returning from these pleasant summers, he devoted himself with renewed enthusiasm to his university lectures. In 1867, Professor Voskresensky was transferred to the University of Kharkov. Mendeleyev, at thirty-two, was elected to the vacant chair of inorganic or general chemistry, a post he was to hold for twenty-three years.

Once he had considered teaching merely a way to earn a living, with time free for his research. Gradually he became passionately dedicated to the instructing of young minds. With his students he was able, as he could not with his wife, to transmit his own awe before the wonders of chemistry.

Avoiding an academic approach, he spoke in an offhand, informal manner. From chemistry he inevitably digressed into related branches of science—astronomy, meteorology, mineralogy, geology, biology and agronomy. He wanted his future scientists to have a sense of perspective, a feeling of the mighty challenge to anyone who would investigate the laws of nature. He instilled them with a love of research, at the same time stressing that science for the sake of science was not enough. Science, to be worthy of its name, must be a servant for all mankind.

In his demonstrations, prepared in advance by himself and his assistants, he produced a veritable bag of magician's tricks—bubbling liquids, flaming colors, explosive reactions. The university now had its own spectroscope. Each of his students had the thrill he had first experienced at Heidelberg of seeing the colored spectra that were distinct for every element.

In the middle of 1867, Mendeleyev was appointed to the committee organizing the Russian Pavilion at the World Industrial Exhibition in Paris. Following the exhibition, he visited factories in France, Germany and Belgium, to study how chemistry was being utilized by industry in these countries. On his return he wrote a large book, with a long title: *The Current Development of Certain Chemical Industries in Application to Russia. The World Exhibition of 1867.*

Intentionally, it was so simply written that even a nonchemist could understand it. He wanted Russian government officials and businessmen to understand the importance of introducing new techniques into Russian industries. Why was it, he demanded angrily, that Russia left untouched all its natural salts, limestone and pyrites—and imported ready-made products containing these same raw materials? He was equally vehement about the reckless burning of valuable forests simply to get ash for soap production. He gave a long list of examples of the backwardness of Russia, at the same time offering suggestions for technological progress. Thus in citing chemical industrial processes, he emphasized the need to produce soda, important in glass manufacture, and the production of textiles.

Unexpectedly an older sister, Ekaterina Kapustin, whom he had not seen since he left Tobolsk, arrived from Siberia. Like Olga, she was now a widow, and she brought with her four children and one grandchild. Mendeleyev gave them a temporary home at Boblovo and later installed them in

St. Petersburg. He was fond of them all but became particularly attached to his twelve-year-old niece, an intelligent and sensitive child called Nadezhda, the Russian word for "hope."

Then another sister, Maria, came with her husband, a former director of the Tomsk high school, and their seven children. Mendeleyev helped them get settled too.

Feozva liked his Siberian relatives and felt comfortable with them, more so in fact than with her husband. In 1868, their second child was born, a daughter they named Olga. Now they had two delightful children, but their marriage was still troubled with dissent. It was not only that they had no intellectual interests in common, and that Feozva had no understanding of the work that engrossed her husband, but also that by temperament and character, they were totally unsuited to each other. They both realized it now. Mendeleyev locked this personal failure within himself. His closest colleagues knew nothing of it as yet.

One project very dear to his heart was to form an organization of Russian scientists, similar to the Royal Society in London. With a student-disciple, Nicolai Menshutkin, he made plans and drew up a list of prospective members, but for a long while they could go no further. They had to get government permission, and this proved difficult. Ever since the Decembrists, the authorities were suspicious of all organizations, including scientific ones. Finally, after long negotiations, official consent was granted.

The charter members of the Russian Chemical Society held their first formal meeting at Mendeleyev's apartment on November 6, 1868, with Mendeleyev presiding as chairman. From this modest beginning, the society expanded to include the leading scientists in all branches of science in Russia. Many important scientific events were first announced at the society meetings. In connection with this work, Mendeleyev carried on an enormous correspondence. It was his brain-child and he never neglected it.

In the same year that the Chemical Society was born, a volume called *Principles of Chemistry* was published. This was Mendeleyev's major book. It went through many editions and was translated into French, German and English. "A veritable treasurehouse of ideas," the British scientist Sir Edward Thorpe called it. "A classic in chemistry."

"It is the function of science," Mendeleyev wrote in *Principles of Chemistry,* "to discover the existence of a general reign of order in nature and to find the causes governing this order. . . . The palace of science needs not only material but a plan, it needs harmony."

To find the "general reign of order in nature" and the plan and harmony in "the palace of science" became his next project. It was not a new undertaking. He had been thinking about it, and working on it off and on, ever since his student days.

7

THE ENIGMA
OF THE ELEMENTS

ALL MATTER WAS MADE UP OF ELEMENTS—WHICH IN NORMAL
temperatures were either gas, liquid or solid. Everyone in
the field of science was in agreement about this. In the loose
terminology that scientists still used, they were referred to
variously as "chemical elements," "simple bodies" or "elementary bodies." An element was defined currently as
"matter in its simplest form," or as "a substance that cannot
be split up by any known means into something simpler."

By the end of 1868, sixty-three substances had been identified as elements. It was truly amazing how many people
had been involved in their discovery and in what remote
and unlikely spots and under what different circumstances
they had been located.

The first pure elements familiar to men were, likely, gold
and copper, which were used to make weapons and orna-
ments in Egypt and Mesopotamia as early as 3400 B.C. The
ancient Greeks knew seven metallic elements: gold, silver,
copper, lead, tin, iron and liquid mercury. For many centuries "seven" retained a mystic significance.

Carbon was known in early times, not as a gas, but in its
solid forms: as charcoal, graphite and sparkling diamonds.

Sulfur, called brimstone (burning stone) in the Bible, was prevalent in volcanic lava. The ancients knew of arsenic in its poisonous compounds but not in its nonpoisonous pure form. The salts of antimony were used medicinally before the Christian era. Arsenic, antimony, as well as bismuth, which are all similar, were identified as separate substances by the alchemists in the Middle Ages.

The alchemists, though they failed in their attempts to transform baser metals into gold, contributed largely to the groundwork of modern chemistry. One of them, a German named Hennig Brand, discovered in 1649 a soft, white, waxy substance which burned with a greenish glow when exposed to air. He called it phosphorus from the Greek words meaning "I bear light." Brand is the first individual credited with the discovery of an element.

In South America, a Spanish naval officer, explorer and scientist, Antonio de Ulloa, discovered platinum about 1735. This rust-resistant silvery metal was considered of little value at the time. Zinc was used in India in 1200 A.D. or before, but its isolation and discovery are credited to the German chemist Andreas Marggraf, in 1745.

Cobalt, which the ancient Babylonians used to color glass blue, was identified as a metal in 1737 by George Brandt. Axel Cronstedt, a Swede, is credited with the discovery of nickel in 1751. The name cobalt comes from the German word for "goblin." Nickel was first called *kuppernickel* or "Old Nick's copper." German miners believed that mischievous spirits lurked in cobalt and nickel ores, from which they tried in vain to get copper.

Early Greek philosophers believed that air was an element—along with earth, water and fire. Many centuries passed before the discovery that matter was not destroyed when wood burned or water evaporated, simply converted into invisible substances. An early seventeenth-century Belgian chemist, Johann Baptist van Helmont, objected to classifying all such invisible substances as air. He invented the word "gas," derived from either the Latin *chaos* or the Dutch word *geest,* meaning ghost.

Five gases were added to the list of elements between 1766 and 1774. Hydrogen, the lightest element, was first isolated by the English recluse Lord Henry Cavendish, whom his colleagues called "the richest of the learned and the most learned of the rich." Oxygen was identified almost simultaneously by Joseph Priestley (an Englishman who believed in the American Revolution) and the Swedish scientist Carl Wilhelm Scheele. Antoine Lavoisier (later guillotined in the French Revolution) verified the existence of this most plentiful of all elements and gave it the name of oxygen. Soon afterward, Cavendish made the momentous discovery that water was not an element but a combination of hydrogen and oxygen.

Nitrogen, first called azote, is credited to Daniel Rutherford, a pupil at Edinburgh University. Carl Scheele, the Swede, isolated fluorine and chlorine, both greenish yellow gases and highly dangerous in concentrated form.

From 1774 to the end of the century, ten more elements were identified. Scheele was responsible for the tough and brittle metal manganese and for molybdenum, which has one of the highest melting points of all metals. Tellurium, a soft metal which paradoxically adds strength to steel, was discovered by Franz von Richenstein. Tungsten, one of the hardest metals, was identified by the d'Elhuja brothers of Spain. Martin Heinrich Klaproth, a professor of chemistry at the University of Berlin, discovered zirconium, a soft, white, crystalline metal, and uranium, which would later launch the atomic age. He also named titanium, which was first found in the sands of the beaches of Cornwall by an English clergyman, Reverend W. Gregor. Yttrium was first investigated by Johan Godalin and was later named after Ytterby, the Swedish town where it was found. Louis Nicolas Vauquelin, the French scientist, was the discoverer in 1797 of beryllium, a steel gray lightweight metal, and of chromium, an exceedingly hard metallic element, outstanding for the many colors of its compounds.

The nineteenth century began with the discovery of niobium, by the English chemist, Charles Hatchett in 1801, and of tantalum the next year by A. G. Ekeburg, a Swedish chemist. Both are corrosion-resistant, malleable, silvery white metals.

In 1803, the year in which John Dalton announced his atomic theory, William Wollaston discovered rhodium and palladium; Berzelius, Klaproth and Wilhelm Hisinger, working separately, identified cerium, and Smithson Tennant found iridium and osmium.

Humphry Davy, the celebrated English scientist, was the first to use electrolysis to isolate certain elements from their compounds. In 1807 and 1808 he identified seven by this method, all important: potassium, sodium, boron, barium, calcium, magnesium and strontium. Also by electrolysis he demonstrated that diamonds are one form of carbon. Davy refused to believe in the existence of atoms and condemned Dalton's theory.

In 1811, the French chemist Bernard Courtois discovered iodine in seaweed. J. August Arfvedson, a Swedish scientist, identified lithium, the lightest of the metallic elements, in 1817. That same year Berzelius identified selenium and Freidrich Stromeyer cadmium. In 1823, Berzelius announced that silicon was an element. Silica sand, which Mendeleyev as a child saw transported to the glass factory, was mainly silicon dioxide, a compound of this element.

In 1826, Antoine J. Balard identified bromine, brownish red in color and the only element except mercury that at normal temperature is a liquid. Its noxious odor caused Justus Liebig to say: "Balard has not discovered bromine as much as bromine has discovered Balard." About the same time, the Danish physicist Hans Christian Oersted (discoverer of the phenomenon of electromagnetism) identified aluminum, an incredibly versatile metal which would be put to thousands of useful purposes.

The next honors went to Sweden. Berzelius identified thorium in 1828. In 1830, N. G. Sefstrom discovered vanadium, which resembles niobium and tantalum. Karl G. Mosander discovered three elements, to be classified as "rare earths," lanthanum in 1839 and erbium and terbium in 1843. Mendeleyev was then nine years old.

C. E. Klaus described ruthenium, a hard metal slightly soluble in acids, in 1844.

No more names were added for fourteen years. Mendeleyev was still in Heidelberg when his two professors, Bunsen and Kirchhoff, identified cesium and rubidium by means of the spectroscope they had invented. In 1861, the Englishman Sir William Crookes discovered thallium. In 1863, Ferdinand Reich and H. T. Richter, using a spectroscope, discovered indium, a soft silvery metal with a spectrum showing two indigo lines. Indium was the sixty-third element to be identified.

In 1868, the French scientist Pierre Janssen went to India to study the spectrum of the sun during an eclipse. By use of a spectroscope it had already been established that certain elements known on earth also existed in the sun's chromosphere. The spectrum that Janssen made during the eclipse showed, among familiar bands of color, one prominent yellow line that did not correspond to the spectrum of any known element. Sir Norman Lockyer in England also noticed this phenomenon and gave the mysterious substance the name of helium, after the Greek word for the sun, *helios.* Though helium was officially the sixty-fourth element discovered, for many years nothing was known of it but its spectrum.

Of the others, at first glance one could be impressed only by their variety. Some were plentiful, such as aluminum, silicon and oxygen, the latter making up about half the atoms on the earth's crust and in the atmosphere. Others, antimony, for instance, were rare. They were metallic or nonmetallic, hard, soft, liquid and gas. They varied in color. Bromine was reddish, phosphorus was white, iodine was gray. About twenty-five were familiar to nearly everyone and had a role in everyday life. The rest included strange names which only a dedicated scientist could remember: molybdenum, tellurium, yttrium, niobium, erbium, selenium . . .

They had been found haphazardly in rocks, minerals and ores, in seaweed, in the ocean and mineral waters, in the atmosphere, in bones and organic matter. Yet nature was not haphazard. "The palace of science needs not only material but a plan, it needs harmony." To Mendeleyev's logical mind it seemed inconceivable that nature had created the elements helter-skelter, without rhyme or reason. Over the years his conviction grew that there was a relationship among them.

Because of that conviction he had kept his notebooks full of miscellaneous information about them. During the writing of *Principles of Chemistry,* he intensified his research.

There was no clearinghouse for the work being done in the world's chemical laboratories. To make certain he was over-looking nothing, he wrote hundreds of letters to foreign labo-ratories, checking the answers he received by innumerable experiments of his own. One day he went out and purchased a large batch of white cards. At the top of each card he wrote the name of each known element, excepting only helium.

To Mendeleyev these sixty-three elements represented a challenge, the greatest and most engrossing of his scientific career. From them—and those yet undiscovered—everything on land or sea or in the atmosphere was formed—all living things and inanimate things, all things created by nature and made by man. It was an overwhelming, awesome thought.

To the uninitiated, it seemed folly to think there might be a relationship among these widely assorted substances. Where would one begin to fathom nature's master plan in their creation?

Mendeleyev began, quite logically, with the atoms—the smallest particles into which an element could be divided and still remain the same substance.

Mystery still surrounded the nature of the tiny atom. Since it could not be seen with the strongest microscope, only by indirect methods could chemists learn anything about it. It was generally believed that atoms were round, but there was no proof of that. Whether they were hard or soft, liquid or solid, or varied in shape and substance with the different elements, was a matter of conjecture. A few scientists had attempted to determine the size of atoms, but the results were far from conclusive.

Nor could anyone say how much an atom weighed, though it appeared that all atoms of the same element weighed the same. True, the atoms of every element had a different weight from the atoms of every other element. This had been expressed as a theory by John Dalton, confirmed by Avogadro's law of gases, and followed through by a host of careful experimenters, who had established atomic weights for all known elements, helium excepted.

The atoms of hydrogen were lighter than those of any other element. By the atomic weight scale in current use, hydrogen had an atomic weight of 1. Oxygen atoms weighed about 16 times as much as hydrogen atoms, and therefore oxygen had an atomic weight of 16. The atoms of the gas chlorine weighed 35.5 times those of hydrogen, which gave chlorine an atomic weight of 35.5. Atomic weights of all the other elements were figured in this same relative manner. The pioneer work of nineteenth-century chemists in atomic weights would stand the test of time, though there were some minor and major discrepancies.

To get the most accurate atomic weights available, Mendeleyev wrote to all the experts in this field. The Belgian scientist Jean Servais Stas, whose painstaking methods of measuring were unequaled, sent him atomic weights for lithium, nitrogen, sodium, sulfur, among others. From Jean Baptiste Dumas, the eminent French scientist, he received atomic weights of calcium, iron, arsenic and strontium. Sir William Crookes, the discoverer of thallium, forwarded him the atomic weight of that element. Kruss Nilson, the Swedish scientist, gave him the atomic weight of thorium. Bohuslav Brauner, a professor at Prague University in Czechoslovakia, provided atomic weights on tellurium, lanthanum and cerium.

All these atomic weights, and others, he verified so far as he could through his own experiments.

On each of his white cards, next to the name of the element he wrote the element's atomic weight. This was his most important clue, and beginning with hydrogen, he arranged his cards in the order of their atomic weights.

Another known fact about atoms was that they united with atoms of other elements, or with atoms of the same element, in definite proportions, to form molecules, the basic particle of a compound. Mendeleyev noted on the cards the nature of some of these compounds. Moreover—and here was a most curious thing—the atoms of some elements formed their molecules in similar ways. Mendeleyev particularly observed that two atoms of certain elements combined readily with one atom of oxygen. In other elements, one atom combined with one oxygen atom. In still others, two atoms, under certain circumstances, combined with five oxygen atoms. There were several more such possible combinations.

Atomicity, he called this phenomenon. Others called it combining power, or valence. In the "atomicity" of an element lay the secret of why certain elements could be substituted for others in a compound. In his search for a pattern within the elements, this uncanny ability of atoms to choose the number of their mates interested Mendeleyev exceedingly.

His white cards contained other information about each element, such as melting point, critical temperature, luster, malleability, density, specific gravity—a compendium of all the data he had accumulated. From them he hoped to extract the hidden code that would unlock the enigma of the elements.

On his laboratory table he dealt the cards out, as though for a game of solitaire, from top to bottom, in vertical columns. Always keeping these columns in the order of the atomic weights of the elements, he rearranged them, lengthened some columns, left blank spaces in others. Sometimes he stared motionless for hours, then made a few more moves, checked his notes, or stopped for another laboratory experiment, on top of the thousands he had already made. At times, on a sheet of paper, he drew a chart of the current arrangement, using symbols for the elements. By the next day this same chart would be almost indecipherable —a mass of crosses and corrections.

Night after night, he played this lonely game, to the utter amazement of Feozva, his sister and any of the other members of his family who ventured to stare at him from the doorway.

Only to his favorite niece, Nadezhda, did he make any attempt to explain what he was trying to do.

One day Feozva sent her in with his tea.

"What are those cards, Uncle?" she asked, frankly curious. "What do they represent?"

He explained that they represented the sixty-three known elements, the building materials out of which everything in the world was made. He told her that all elements were composed of atoms and that, for some reason, the atoms of some elements were heavier or lighter than the atoms of other elements.

"How very interesting!" Nadezhda, who was fourteen now, slender and dark-haired, stared intently at the cards, as though she expected to see their atoms jumping up and down. "What are you doing with the elements, Uncle?"

"I am putting them in order," he said, with a trace of pride. "Arranged by their atomic weights, there is a rhythm to them. At regular intervals, or periods, elements show marked similarities." He spoke in the tone of one making the most earthshaking announcement.

"What a responsibility!" exclaimed Nadezhda. "What a great responsibility, Uncle, to put the elements in order!"

The work he was doing was not without precedent. There had been a few others who had been struck with the fact that some elements were similar and that these similarities had some relation to atomic weight.

In the 1820's, Johann Wolfgang Doebereiner had named several sets of "triads." One triad was chlorine, iodine and bromine, which were all nonmetals and extremely active— that is, they formed compounds easily. Berzelius had named them halogen or "salt-former" elements, because, combined with hydrogen, they produced acids that acted readily on most elements to form salts.

Lithium, sodium and potassium, another "triad," were all light and soft metals that melted at low temperatures and were violently explosive in contact with water. They were called alkali metals. Then there were phosphorus, arsenic and antimony, which were all soft elements, capable of forming poisonous compounds, and which, in pure state isolated from their compounds, assumed several different forms.

The oddest thing about these triads was that if one added together the atomic weights of the first and third, then divided by two, the result was the approximate atomic weight of the second. Thus, the atomic weight of chlorine was 35.5 and of iodine 127, a total of 162.5. Divide this by two to get the "arithmetic mean," and the result was 81.25, very close to bromine's given atomic weight of 80.

"Doebereiner's triads" aroused some speculation, though most scientists contended that their resemblance was accidental. Dumas and the Englishman William Odling, among a few others, extended the triads to include other elements. On the whole, the making of "Doebereiner's triads" was considered a scientific amusement and nothing more.

Two men attempted a more comprehensive chart of the elements.

In 1866, John A. R. Newlands, an Englishman, presented a daring—some said impudent—paper to the British Chemical Society. The paper stated that if all the elements were arranged in order of their atomic weights, the elements at each interval of eight would be similar. He likened this sequence to the octaves of a piano keyboard: "This peculiar relationship I propose to provisionally term the *law of octaves.*"

His colleagues were quick to point out that despite a few similarities, there were many unharmonious discords among his "octaves." That evening, it is said, the usually staid and sedate society membership fairly rocked with laughter. One member sarcastically suggested that Newlands might have more success if he arranged the elements *alphabetically.* Newlands was so crushed by the mocking reaction to his law of octaves that he quit scientific research for good.

A Frenchman named Beguyer de Chancourtois, noting certain similarities among the elements, arranged them in order of their atomic weights in a winding spiral, seeking to place similar elements one under another on this spiral. His effort was no more successful than that of Newlands.

Mendeleyev knew of Doebereiner's triads but at this time was unfamiliar with the work of Chancourtois and Newlands. It would not have mattered if he had know of it. The difference between him and these others was that he was not merely trying to group elements by their similarities. He was seeking a fundamental law of nature.

Nor could he be content with any arrangement that

looked neat and pretty on paper. He could not force his elements to fit in where they did not rightly belong. The problem that seemed relatively simple in regard to the lighter elements became more complicated with the heavier elements. There came a day when he knew he had gone as far as he could for the time being. He was not yet satisfied, but he had done his best.

He pinned all his cards upon his wall and then stood off and looked at them. But he made no more changes. Instead he drew out a fresh sheet of paper. Across the top of it he wrote in neat script, "An Outline of the System of the Elements." Once more he made a chart, this time without further corrections.

The day after he completed "An Outline of the System of the Elements," Mendeleyev took it to the printer to have copies made. These he mailed to the members of the Russian Chemical Society. The next weeks he spent preparing a paper to explain his chart, for presentation to the society meeting on March 18, 1869. The strain of the last months of arduous mental labor was beginning to tell on him. He had lost weight and was beginning to cough again. A few days before the meeting he took a walk along the Neva to clear his head.

The river was still frozen. Girl skaters in full and brightly colored skirts pirouetted on the ice with their more sedately clad escorts. A group of Lapps in picturesque native costumes rode by in a sleigh drawn by reindeer; they had no doubt come to trade their winter furs for stable goods. Further on, a battalion of the Emperor's guard were performing maneuvers on the river's frozen surface.

Only half-seeing, Mendeleyev watched the bright panorama. His mind was on the paper he intended to read to the Russian Chemical Society. Written for a scientifically

AN OUTLINE OF THE SYSTEM OF THE ELEMENTS
[1869]

			Ti 50 Titanium	Zr 90 Zirconium	? 100
			V 51 Vanadium	Nb 94 Niobium	Ta 182 Tantalum
			Cr 52 Chromium	Mo 96 Molybdenum	W 186 Tungsten
			Mn 55 Manganese	Rh 104.4 Rhodium	Pt 197.4 Platinum
			Fe 56 Iron	Ru 104.4 Ruthenium	Ir 198 Iridium
			Ni-Co 59 Nickel-Cobalt	Pd 106.6 Palladium	Os 199 Osmium
H 1 Hydrogen			Cu 63.4 Copper	Ag 108 Silver	Hg 200 Mercury
	Be 9.4 Beryllium	Mg 24 Magnesium	Zn 65.2 Zinc	Cd 112 Cadmium	
	B 11 Boron	Al 27 Aluminum	? 68	U 116 Uranium	Au 197? Gold
	C 12 Carbon	Si 28 Silicon	? 70	Sn 118 Tin	
	N 14 Nitrogen	P 31 Phosphorus	As 75 Arsenic	Sb 122 Antimony	Bi 210? Bismuth
	O 16 Oxygen	S 32 Sulfur	Se 79.4 Selenium	Te 128? Tellurium	
	F 19 Fluorine	Cl 35.5 Chlorine	Br 80 Bromine	I 127 Iodine	
Li 7 Lithium	Na 23 Sodium	K 39 Potassium	Rb 85.4 Rubidium	Cs 133 Cesium	Tl 204 Thallium
		Ca 40 Calcium	Sr 87.6 Strontium	Ba 137 Barium	Pb 207 Lead
		? 45	Ce 92 Cerium		
		Er? 56 Erbium	La 94 Lanthanum		
		Yt? 60 Yttrium	Di 95		
		In 75.6? Indium	Th 118? Thorium		

Note: Mendeleyev's original chart contained only element symbols, atomic weights—and question marks. For clarity, the full names of the elements are included. The rectangular boxes show "Doebereiner's triads."

trained audience, it lacked the simplicity of style and homely analogies of his student lectures. That did not trouble him so much as that, in one short piece, it was impossible to encompass all the thinking and planning that had gone into this work.

His colleagues, for instance, would surely demand why he had taken it on himself to change beryllium from its accepted atomic weight of 13.7 to 9.4 and given calcium an atomic weight of 40 instead of 20, as others did. He would have to explain to them that he had taken the liberty of making these changes because, in view of the properties of these two elements, he was sure the established weights were wrong. . . .

He was looking forward to the meeting. Now that he would be able to share with other scientists the project he had kept to himself so long, he was practically exploding with it. He was strangely elated at the prospect, almost lightheaded, much as Sir Humphry Davy must have felt when he first breathed "nitrous oxide in a state of purity," the substance popularly called "laughing gas."

Once more he went over his paper in his mind—he knew it by heart—and it occurred to him that in several places he could improve it, elucidate his meaning, make it more convincing. Walking so rapidly that he was coughing and choking with the exertion, he hurried home.

Feozva was waiting at the door.

"Are you mad, Dmitri Ivanovitch, to go out in freezing weather without your greatcoat?"

"I had not noticed," he admitted honestly.

She looked at him more closely. "You are feverish."

"I am not."

He strode past her to his study to make the changes that had seemed so urgent shortly before. But once at his desk, he did nothing. He ached all over, and the ideas that had seemed crystal clear during his walk were nebulous. He was hardly aware how he got himself to bed or when Feozva brought in a doctor to examine him.

"Bronchitis," the doctor diagnosed. "And a run-down condition, too much work, too little sleep, and probably not enough to eat. He needs rest, complete rest."

"I tried," Feozva said, weeping. "Doctor, I brought his tray in every evening. Was I to blame if half the time he left it untouched? You cannot imagine what it is to live with such a man."

Those were the last words Mendeleyev heard before he dozed off in restless slumber.

8

THE BIRTH OF THE PERIODIC
LAW–MARCH 18, 1869

"I REGRET TO ANNOUNCE," SAID THE CHAIRMAN OF THE RUS-
sian Chemical Society at their meeting of March 18, 1869,
"that our esteemed member D. I. Mendeleyev, is suffering
from an indisposition. Accordingly, his paper, 'An Outline
of the System of the Elements, Based on Their Atomic
Weights and Chemical Affinities,' will be read by N. A.
Menshutkin."

Menshutkin, who had been first Mendeleyev's student and
was now his colleague, was more than a little troubled at
the assignment. He knew how much this particular paper
meant to Mendeleyev, though he had not had time to read
it and felt ill-equipped to act as his proxy on this occasion.
But Mendeleyev from his sickbed had insisted that he and
no one else must present it, and he could hardly refuse. It
was after all an honor for a young man still in his early
twenties to represent Russia's leading chemist. With more
assurance than he felt he mounted the rostrum and began:

"In undertaking to prepare a textbook called *Principles of
Chemistry*, I wished to establish some sort of system of
simple bodies in which their distribution is not guided by

96

chance, as might be thought instinctively, but by some sort of definite and exact principle. . . ."

Unfamiliar with the material, Menshutkin slurred some words, stumbled over others, but for the most part continued conscientiously.

". . . The numerical data for simple bodies are limited at the present time. . . . Such properties as optical, or even electrical or magnetic, cannot in the end serve as a support of a system because one and the same body can show different values for these properties, depending on the state in which they occur. . . . Anyone understands that no matter how the properties of a simple body may change in the free state, *something* remains constant, and when the elements form compounds, this *something* has a material value and establishes the characteristics of the compounds which include the given element. . . ."

"What a pity!" a member murmured to his neighbor. "What a pity Dmitri Ivanovitch could not be here to read his own paper, with the enthusiasm he must feel for it."

"The first attempt which I made in this way," Menshutkin plodded on in a monotonous tone, "was the following: I selected the bodies with the lowest atomic weights and arranged them in the order of the size of the atomic weights. This showed that there existed a period in the properties of the simple bodies, and even in terms of their atomicity the elements followed each other in the order of the arithmetic succession of the size of their atoms. . . ."

"Atomicity? Just what does he mean by atomicity?" a man down front barked in a loud whisper.

His companion scowled and put his finger to his lips. Someone in the audience coughed and then someone else, but Menshutkin read on doggedly as words and whole phrases were blotted out:

". . . In the arrangement of elements with atoms greater than 100 we meet an entirely analogous continuous order: silver, 108; cadmium, 112; uranium, 116. . . . It has been shown that lithium, sodium, potassium . . . are related to each other as are carbon, silicon . . . or as are nitrogen, phosphorus. . . . This at once raises the question whether the properties of the elements are expressed by their atomic weights and whether a system can be based on them. An attempt at such a system follows. . . ."

Two young men brought in a blackboard in which the chart of Mendeleyev was chalked in large letters. One of them stumbled and the disturbance drowned out a few more words.

". . . leads to the conclusion that the distribution of the elements according to their atomic weights does not disturb the natural similarities which exist between the elements but, on the contrary, shows them directly. . . . All the comparisons which I have made in this direction lead me to conclude that *the size of the atomic weight determines the nature of the elements.* . . ."

Menshutkin had raised his voice slightly at the last phrase. The coughing had quieted down. Everyone had heard it clearly. Two learned members in the rear exchanged meaningful glances. The brilliant Mendeleyev had gone a little too far, those glances said. How, in the name of all creation, could he actually believe and proclaim that atomic weights alone could determine whether an element was gold or hydrogen, iron or aluminum?

Menshutkin was nearing the end:

". . . In conclusion, I consider it advisable to recapitulate the results of the above work.

"One. Elements arranged according to the size of their atomic weights show clear *periodic* properties."

(Not everyone grasped that Mendeleyev was referring to the similar properties of the elements at regular intervals along the atomic weight scale.)

"Two. Elements which are similar in chemical function either have atomic weights which lie close together (like platinum, iridium, osmium) or show an increase in atomic weight (like potassium, rubidium, cesium). . . .

"Three. Comparisons of the elements or their groups in terms of size of their atomic weights establish their so-called 'atomicity' and, to some extent, differences in chemical character. . . ."

Again that puzzling word "atomicity."

"Four. The simple bodies which are most widely distributed in nature have small atomic weights. . . ."

No one could quarrel with that. Hydrogen and oxygen were the proof.

"Five. The size of the atomic weight determines the character of the element, just as the size of the molecule determines the properties of the complex body.

"Six. We should still expect to discover many *unknown* simple bodies; for example, those similar to aluminum and silicon, elements with atomic weights of 65 to 75."

The significance of this amazing statement missed everyone, even Menshutkin.

"Seven. Some *analogies* of the elements are discovered from the size of the weights of their atoms. . . ."

The audience, patient for the most part, was becoming restless and weary. Menshutkin, sensing this, saw with relief that there was one more paragraph.

"The purpose of my paper will be entirely attained if I succeed in turning the attention of investigators to the same relationships in the size of atomic weights of non-similar elements, which have, as far as I know, been almost entirely neglected until now. Assuming that in problems of this nature lies the solution of one of the most important questions of our science, I myself, as my time will permit, will turn to a comparative study of lithium, beryllium, and boron."

It was over at last. Had Mendeleyev been present, there would have been a question and discussion period. Menshutkin, explaining that he knew no more than he had read, begged them to hold their inquiries until the next meeting when Mendeleyev would be there. The meeting broke up, and the members filed into an adjoining room where tea and cakes were waiting for them.

As they drank and talked, Menshutkin wandered from group to group, hoping to hear some remark that he could repeat to his sick friend as proof of the interest the paper had aroused. One man had spread out his copy of "An Outline of the System of the Elements" and was apparently discussing it with his colleagues.

"A curious thing," he was saying as Menshutkin approached. "Note how many blank spaces he has left. And all these question marks. About a dozen of them. If he was that uncertain, he should have waited."

Menshutkin walked off to join two of his University of St. Petersburg colleagues. They at least should realize that if Mendeleyev put question marks in his system, there must be a sound reason for it.

"Mendeleyev hates chaos, even in nature," he heard one of them say.

The other chuckled.

Menshutkin continued his eavesdropping for a few minutes, but by this time the members were discussing other subjects. There was no point in staying any longer, and he left. He had promised Mendeleyev to give a full report of the meeting, but he did not know what he would say.

Mendeleyev's wife, a timid little woman with melancholy eyes, let him in.

"How is he, Madame Mendeleyev?" he asked of Feozva.

"Better, I think. He wants to see you."

Unhappily he followed her down the long hall. He could hardly tell the professor that everyone was spellbound. No one could fool Dmitri Ivanovitch and get away with it.

Mendeleyev was propped up in his featherbed, a sheaf of papers before him, looking like a trapped lion. His two sisters, Ekaterina and Maria, who had come to help Feozva, were hovering over him. All three women slipped out of the room as Menshutkin entered.

"*Akh,* my good friend, how kind of you to come," Mendeleyev said, beaming at him. "This atmosphere of coddling women is intolerable. The truth is there's nothing wrong with me." His voice was rasping. "Yet they pour medicines down my throat until I gag."

"You're looking fine, Dmitri Ivanovitch."

Menshutkin waited for the expected question about the meeting. It did not come.

"I have decided to call them eka-aluminum and eka-silicon," Mendeleyev confided conspiratorially.

Was the professor delirious? Menshutkin had not the slightest idea what he was talking about.

"Eka-aluminum and eka-silicon," Mendeleyev repeated. "Eka is Sanskrit for 'first.' I am referring to my paper, where I said that two new elements would be found, similar to aluminum and silicon and following them on the periodic table, elements with atomic weights of about 65 to 75. I will give them these names temporarily, for whoever discovers them will have the right to name them."

Menshutkin could hardly believe his ears. "You say that you already know the atomic weights of two elements not yet discovered?"

"Naturally. Did you not listen to my paper when you read it?" Mendeleyev asked, grinning. "There will also be a new element following boron, which I will call eka-boron. I am working out the properties of these three elements now. There will be others. Is there any rule in nature which states there shall be just sixty-three elements and no more?"

Menshutkin was utterly flabbergasted. Loyally, he told himself that the professor was a genius, but he did not doubt that the rest of the world would judge him completely mad, once they saw his paper in print. How could anyone describe the properties of a substance never seen on earth?

"It is quite simple once you grasp the fundamental principle," Mendeleyev said, as though reading his mind. "The fundamental principle that the properties of the elements are the periodic functions of their atomic weights."

It sounded so fantastic, Menshutkin was at a loss for something to say. Eventually he murmured,

"Remarkable! Simply remarkable, Dmitri Ivanovitch."

For Menshutkin it had been a long and trying day.

In the future, students would be taught that on March 18, 1869, Dmitri Mendeleyev, the "Russian patriarch," announced the periodic law of the elements. In reality, like many great days in history, none of those who shared in its events recognized its full significance. Menshutkin went home to bed. In the kitchen of the Mendeleyev apartment, Feozva and her two sisters-in-law, Maria and Ekaterina, drank tea and spoke of household matters. Mendeleyev himself—not a "patriarch" but a young man not yet thirty-five—fumed at the illness that kept him confined to bed, as he continued to make notes on the properties of three yet undiscovered elements—eka-aluminum, eka-silicon and eka-boron.

Mendeleyev's paper, just as Menshutkin had read it, appeared the next month in the first issue of the *Journal* of the Russian Chemical Society. Contrary to Menshutkin's fears, it did not provoke derision. Except for a small note in a German journal, the foreign press ignored it. Even with the Russians, it made no more stir than a fallen leaf on a still pool.

In 1871, the second volume of *Principles of Chemistry* was published. Chapter 15 contained the first full statement of the periodic law. In this chapter Mendeleyev mentioned J. A. R. Newlands, author of the law of octaves, de Chancourtois, who had arranged the elements in a spiral, as well as the German scientist Lothar Meyer, who, like Mendeleyev, had found inspiration from Cannizarro at the Congress of Karlsruhe. Meyer too had been working on a system of the elements and in 1870 had published a chart similar to that of Mendeleyev.

"I consider it well to observe that no law of nature, however general, has been established all at once," Mendeleyev wrote in giving these three the credit due them. "Its recognition is always preceded by many hints."

Two years after his paper had been read by Menshutkin, the Russian Chemical Society *Journal* published "The Natural System of the Elements" along with a greatly revised periodic table.

In the new version he reversed the plan of his first chart and listed the elements in order of their increased atomic weights in horizontal columns, and elements in order of their periodic similarities in vertical columns (a form that future generations of scientists would follow). He called the vertical columns of similar elements "groups" and the horizontal lines "periods."

In his 1869 chart he had changed the established atomic weights of two elements and questioned others. Now he boldly made more changes, seventeen in all. He reversed the atomic weights of tellurium and iodine, so that tellurium would fit into the group headed by oxygen, and iodine would fall in line with fluorine, chlorine and bromine. He reversed gold and platinum, as well as cobalt and nickel, for a similar reason. His most drastic changes were to double the atomic weight of thorium, from 116 to 232, and of uranium, from 120 to 240, showing it to be the heaviest of the known elements. Time would justify him for all this tampering.

He left blank spaces for sixteen new elements, and for six of them, including eka-aluminum, eka-silicon and eka-boron, he gave approximate atomic weights and described certain of their properties. He prophesied five "transuranic" elements—elements with a higher atomic weight than uranium—one of his most amazing predictions.

Foreign scientists read Mendeleyev's 1871 paper in the German translation (it was not translated into English until 1879), and the word spread that a scientist in backward Russia with an unpronounceable name had risked his reputation in some daring guesswork. The Russian Chemical Society achieved some renown from the publicity. Letters came in turn from the English Chemical Society, the French Academy of Science, and the faraway Smithsonian Institution in Washington, D.C., all suggesting an exchange of scientific publications. The Russian scientists were jubilant at this sign of recognition from the outside world.

As paper after paper on the system of the chemical elements had appeared, the attitude of a good portion of the

Russian Chemical Society membership had changed from indifference to enthusiasm. Some were secretly worried. In spite of the logic of the periodic law, did it not in the long run provoke more questions than it answered? The real and final solution seemed as far away as ever.

"The properties of the elements are the periodic functions of their atomic weights," Mendeleyev had told Menshutkin, and repeated it in his writing, again and again.

"Would you say that this is a theory or a hypothesis?" a colleague asked.

"I answered that in my last paper," Mendeleyev said. "The establishment of a law of nature does not take place when its significance is recognized, but only when it has been confirmed by experiment, which the man of science must consider as the only proof of the correctness of his conjectures and episodes."

"And what proof do you expect, Dmitri Ivanovitch?"

"Proof?" Mendeleyev shrugged. "I have no need of proof. The laws of nature, unlike the laws of grammar, admit of no exception." He added, slyly, "I suppose when my unknown elements are found, more people will pay us attention. That will start the ball rolling."

9

THE PROOF

————————————————————————————

ALEXANDRE BORODIN, MENDELEYEV'S FRIEND OF HEIDELBERG
and his student days, was now a distinguished professor at
the St. Petersburg Academy of Medicine. Nor had he for-
saken his music. With Rimsky-Korsakov and Modest Mu-
sorgski, he had formed a group dedicated to give Russia a
national music, based in part on folk songs and in part on
their own creative efforts to interpret musically Russia's
turbulent history. Borodin's first symphony was produced
on January 16, 1869, two months before the birth of the
periodic table. Since then he had been working on an opera,
the story of the Russian epic of Prince Igor.

He and Mendeleyev continued their friendship, though
they saw each other rarely. At a chance meeting Borodin
insisted Mendeleyev come visit him; he had something he
wished to discuss.

Borodin and his wife Catherine, the pretty pianist he had
met at Heidelberg, lived in a long sprawling apartment in
the Academy of Medicine building, filled with children,
cats and usually an assortment of relatives who arrived unexpectedly, slept on sofas and were made welcome as long
as they cared to stay. Students seeking advice, or fellow
musicians wanting companionship, arrived at all hours.
Mendeleyev could not help comparing the informal at-

mosphere, and its currents of laughter, music, affection and harmony, with his own home life, where he and Feozva lived as polite strangers. Sternly, he told himself he could never stand such disorder, but he could not help feeling a pang of envy.

While Catherine served tea, Borodin launched into an account of his latest activity. With two colleagues he had founded the Women's Medical College of St. Petersburg, the first of its kind in Russia. It had taken several years to get the government's consent. Did Mendeleyev have any idea how many young women were now flocking to St. Petersburg, working as translators, as bookbinders, at anything they could get, in the hope that institutions of higher education would open their doors to them? A few professors took the risk of giving them private lessons, and the Women's Medical College was only a small step in the right direction. It seemed a shame. It was his opinion, Borodin said, that women were certainly as intelligent as men, that is, if they were given the same opportunities.

"Do you not think so, Dmitri Ivanovitch?"

"No," said Mendeleyev. "Women are not all stupid, but I would not say they are as intelligent as men."

Nevertheless, Borodin's story started him thinking, and shortly afterward Mendeleyev opened free classes in chemistry to women students. Women might not be as intelligent as men, but he saw no reason why they should be forbidden a chance to learn, if that was what they wanted. Certain government officials were not at all pleased.

The reforms of Alexander II had bogged down badly. Neither the landlords nor the former serfs were satisfied with the results of the emancipation. Landlords who had had to give up half of their land complained that they were reimbursed too slowly. The peasants, impoverished by exorbitant taxation, found their new freedom a hollow victory.

Two attempts were made on the Tsar's life. Since one of his would-be assassins had been a student at Kazan University, all university students came under close police scrutiny. As Minister of Education, the Tsar appointed Count A. D. Tolstoy—a narrow, bigoted, ignorant man, who disliked all young people, especially educated ones—to keep students from thinking dangerous thoughts.

Mendeleyev was elected member of a commission to advise the Count. It proved the most unpleasant and unrewarding assignment of his career.

There was a meeting when Tolstoy (quite opposite in character to Leo Tolstoy, the novelist) brought out a sheaf of papers, no doubt provided by the police, about the "To the People" movement.

"Do you know what is happening?" the Count shrieked. "Young men, and even women, many from wealthy homes, are pouring into the slums, fishing villages, farm villages. They work as laborers and they live like laborers."

"So?" commented Mendeleyev dryly. "And what are they doing that for?"

"They are *teaching* the people." The Count's face turned dark red. "They are teaching peasants and workers all they know themselves."

"And is that wrong?" asked Mendeleyev mildly. "Whenever I go to Boblovo I ride in the third-class compartment so I can be with the muzhiks, who are very good people. They ask me and I tell them about science. They may not understand very much but they are most interested."

"You are being facetious, sir," the Count said coldly. "If you don't see the harm of this movement, you should face the facts. Naturally, we are taking steps to halt it. The students may dress like beggars, but our agents spot them easily by the way they talk and walk. So they end up in the Fortress of St. Peter and St. Paul, where they can do their preaching to the dungeon walls—or even better in Siberia."

With difficulty, Mendeleyev restrained himself from expressing his disgust and shame, but there were other meetings when he failed completely to keep his temper.

The Minister of Education had a special aversion to science, which he contended produced a "superficial and materialistic outlook on life" and turned students into "nihilists." He believed that Russian literature and history were taught in "too liberal" a manner. On the other hand, he approved greater emphasis on Latin and Greek, particularly grammar.

On each of these points Mendeleyev fought him bitterly. It was useless. The commission had no power at all, and the Minister of Education had the full authority of the Tsar. The teaching of science was banned from grammar schools. The examinations in the classics were made so severe that thousands of students failed them and had to leave school without their diplomas, some to join the "To the People" movement and the growing ranks of revolutionaries.

Professor Zinin met Mendeleyev stomping gloomily through the university halls.

"I hear you've been having some disagreements with our new Minister of Education."

"That ignoramus!" Mendeleyev snorted.

"I may agree with you completely," Zinin said, seriously, "but I feel I should warn you that you have made a powerful enemy."

"So be it," he grunted. "I would not be able to hold up my head if he were my friend."

He was not worried about Count Tolstoy's opinion, since it never occurred to him there could be any doubt about his own patriotism. His whole life was dedicated to building up the image of Russian science in the world, to creating future Russian scientists, to advancing Russian industry through science. What had he to fear?

Between 1869 and 1875 he published dozens of papers. Some were the result of pure research: "Heat Capacity and Complexity of the Carbon Molecule"; "Specific Volumes of Hydrocarbon Combinations"; "On Crystallization and Water Trapped During the Process"; "The Atomic Weight of Yttrium." Others had to do with earth analysis and agriculture. There was one article on manufacture of cheese in Artels. He wrote on the need for enlarging the St. Petersburg University laboratory, for improving Russian high schools—this in direct opposition to Count Tolstoy. And for the *Juridical News* he contributed a piece on examination of court matters.

He had never lost his early interest in gases, and in the early 1870's began intensive work on their properties and behavior at high and low pressures. The Russian Technical Society invited him to speak about this work.

"What led you to the study of gases?" one of his audience asked.

"African explorers do not go to those parts of the continent that have already become civilized," he said. "They try to go where no foot has trod before them. It is the same with a research chemist. He is drawn to unexplored territory."

With aid provided by the Technical Society, he equipped and staffed a special laboratory for his study of gases. From his experiments, he produced an equation on the state of perfect gases in advance of any other work on the subject.

A book of 263 pages, *Resilience of Gases,* published in 1875, covered the high points of his investigation.

His work on gases led him "willy-nilly," as he put it, to meteorology and a study of atmospheric and weather conditions. It occurred to him that balloons might be equipped to gather information about the upper strata of the atmosphere, and with this in mind he made designs for a balloon with a hermetically sealed gondola, inside of which the pilot would breath "compressed air" and "make observations and steer the balloon in safety." He presented the design at a Russian Chemical Society meeting in 1875, but though the members were impressed, no action was taken. He also drew up plans for a dirigible with metal skin and an internal combustion engine, and invented a highly sensitive barometer which could accurately record heights above sea level.

He foresaw that air travel would have an important role in the world of the future and wanted his own country to be prepared for it:

"In other countries there are many coasts along the ocean of water," he wrote. "In Russia such areas are comparatively small, but on the other hand, she possesses greater shores along the free ocean of air than any other country. For Russia, therefore, it is more suitable to take possession of this ocean, the more so that this bloodless conquest will constitute an epoch with which the newest history of culture will begin."

As a scientist he was concerned with a "new and unexplored branch of science"—spiritualism. In darkened rooms mediums went into trances, and spectators sat enthralled as tables were tipped, voices came from nowhere, and apparitions of relatives from the land of the dead were materialized. Attending seances provided a welcome escape from the country's social problems, but this fad was not limited to the uneducated. In fact, some of Mendeleyev's colleagues, including his brillant protégé, Butelerov, believed firmly in psychic phenomena. Conservative scientific journals published many articles on this new *science*. Mendeleyev, who considered table-tipping extremely unscientific, disputed hotly with the authors of these articles. After some fiery discussions, he offered to investigate spiritualism. A commission of distinguished scientists agreed to assist him.

Four mediums consented to comply with the controlled conditions of the investigation. One of them was the famous Madame Blavadskaya, daughter of a German nobleman, who had studied occultism in Tibet and India. Mendeleyev provided the mediums with all the materials they wished, including jars, slates and tables, but insisted on the right to light a lamp when he chose and to make chemical tests on the spot. Nineteen seances in all were held, the first few in his apartment.

The details of his investigation were published in a 382-page book, *Information for Critical Judgment of Spiritualism*. "Spiritualist phenomena, so-called," he wrote in conclusion, "operate best at night or in the dark, when deception cannot be so readily noticed." The four mediums, the best in the world, had failed to convince him. The only spirit in which he would believe was the "spirit of free human inquiry."

All royalties from his book on spiritualism were donated to "the construction of a balloon and in general for the study of meteorological phenomena of the upper layers of the atmosphere."

In these last busy years, his periodic table had been of necessity pushed into the background. The controversy that had flared up after the publication of his first papers gradually subsided.

On the night of August 27, 1875, a young French chemist, Lecoq de Boisbaudran, was doing chemical analysis on a zinc blend at the Pierrefitte mine in the Argeles Valley in the French Pyrenees. One of his experiments was to set aflame a small amount of the blend and pass it through a spectroscope. The spectrum included a brilliant violet line belonging to no known element. He repeated his tests over and over, and always found the same mysterious violet line.

Excitedly he sent off a letter to Paris, addressed to his former professor, Dr. Charles Wurtz, telling of the discovery of "traces of the probable existence of a new simple body in the products of the chemical analysis of zinc blend . . ."

Dr. Wurtz had sufficient confidence in de Boisbaudran to read the letter to the French Academy of Science. This was on September 20. Shortly afterward, de Boisbaudran succeeded in isolating a small quantity of his "new simple body" by electrolysis, finding it to be a steel-gray metal resembling aluminum. He named it gallium after his native country, which the Romans had called Gaul.

A month or so later, Mendeleyev was struggling through a French scientific journal, when he suddenly let out such a whoop that Feozva came running from her part of the apartment.

"What's the matter? Have you hurt yourself?"

"Nothing is the matter!" he bellowed joyously. "I have just learned that a Frenchman has discovered eka-aluminum."

"More science?" she asked, resignedly.

"Yes, science," he said, subsiding. For a moment he had forgotten how that very word bored her.

She turned and went out of the room.

His small daughter, curious about the uproar, was peering from the doorway. Mendeleyev spied her.

"Come here, Olga. Would you like to hear a story."

"Oh, yes, Papa." Eagerly she climbed on his lap.

"Once upon a time," he began, "there lived a Tsar who ruled over a country called the Land of Scientific Knowledge. The Tsar, who had a beard like your father, wanted very much to find a treasure. The treasure was called 'I don't know what,' and it was located in a place called 'I don't know where.' He summoned all the bright young men in his kingdom and described 'I don't know what' to them and promised that the first man who found it would receive half the Land of Scientific Knowledge.

"The young men walked away from him, shaking their heads. 'The Tsar has gone mad,' they said. How could anyone find 'I don't know what' in 'I don't know where'? They did not even bother to look.

"Years passed. All the young men had forgotten about the Tsar's offer. If he had not been a patient man he would have lost hope. Then one day another young man from a far province happened upon a substance no one had ever seen on earth before. I will not attempt to describe it except to say that when you set fire to it and held it up to a crystal, a bright violet line appeared. 'I have found "I don't know what," ' cried the young man, very pleased. In time the Tsar heard about it and knew that this young man was entitled to half the Land of Scientific Knowledge."

"Is that the end of the story?" asked Olga, disappointed.

"I don't think that it is," her father said, smugly. "I think it is only the beginning."

The minutes of the November 6, 1875, meeting of the Russian Chemical Society record: "D. Mendeleyev drew attention to the fact that the element recently discovered by L. de Boisbaudran and called by him gallium, both by the method of its discovery (spectral analysis of the spark) and by its properties as so far observed, coincides with eka-aluminum, the certainty of whose existence and properties of which were described four years ago by Mendeleyev on the basis of the periodic law. If gallium is identical with eka-aluminum then it will have an atomic weight of 68 and a density of 5.9."

In due time de Boisbaudran confirmed that by his calculations the atomic weight of gallium was 68, though tests indicated that its density was only 4.7. (Later, measurements established gallium's density at 5.91, very close to Mendeleyev's "guess.") Regardless of slight discrepancies, the whole scientific world was now alerted that one of the prophecies of the Russian "patriarch"—as foreigners still called the forty-one-year-old scientist—had come true. The periodic law must now be taken seriously by everyone.

Just at the time of this scientific triumph, Mendeleyev's marriage, never a satisfactory one, reached a crisis. The two children whom he and Feozva hoped would bring them together had only widened the distance between them. All the love Mendeleyev could not give his wife, he lavished on his son and daughter. Feozva, justifiably, found this hard to bear and accused him of spoiling the children. There were arguments. The situation became unbearable for both, and they decided to separate.

Feozva would stay at Boblovo in the winter when he was in St. Peterburg and return in the summer when he was on their farm. But she insisted on keeping the children with her. It was only fair, she argued. He had his work. She had only her duties as a mother.

Despite his preoccupation with his work, he had always

had time for his children. To lose them was the hardest blow. Loneliness, his old companion, returned. He told himself he would have to learn to accept it.

The next year, in July of 1876, he took the longest trip of his life. His destination was the United States of America, to which the Russian government had sent him to study recent developments in the oil industry.

Thousands of foreign visitors were flocking to American shores that year to share in the celebration of the hundredth anniversary of American independence at the Philadelphia Centennial Exhibition. The arrival of the creator of the periodic table passed almost unnoticed. In New York, a few scientific societies, on being informed of his presence, hastily organized receptions in Mendeleyev's honor. The tall bearded Russian with the shaggy mane of hair and the extraordinarily high forehead was an impressive guest, but communication was difficult. Dmitri Ivanovitch Mendeleyev—a name to make Americans stumble—knew a smattering of English and could only nod pleasantly at the praise his hosts heaped on him.

He went on to Titusville, in northwest Pennsylvania, where the discovery of oil in 1859 had started an oil rush parallel to the California gold rush. There he visited refineries, collected samples and, with the aid of interpreters, interviewed engineers and production men. Keenly observant as always, he jotted down both his favorable and unfavorable impressions. He was surprised that the drilling of oil was not more mechanized and that so little research had been done to improve the methods of refining. America was suffering a depression, and unemployed men crowded the oil fields begging for jobs, some of which were being given to children, who were paid less. The oil boom, which should have brought widespread prosperity, had been marred by cutthroat competition and some corruption. Yet with all its failings, the new American oil industry was a tremendously vital thing. The oilmen Mendeleyev met were mostly under forty, young and energetic and filled with pride and enthusiasm for their work.

Curious about the nature of the terrain in oil-rich regions, Mendeleyev studied rock formations in the Alleghenies, making notes as to how these mountains compared with the Caucasians. Beyond the Alleghenies, he learned of a development that impressed him greatly. Here men had sunk shafts for oil, but instead had obtained gas. Now they were putting this gas to practical industrial uses, building pipelines to transport it hundreds of miles. "This can be done at Baku," he noted.

In the last days of his tour, he stopped in Philadelphia, where he ignored the centennial and spent most of his time in a factory producing petroleum by-products.

The bustle and flurry of Titusville stimulated him to renewed efforts for the Russian oil industry. On his return to his own country, he invented a new method of fractional refining "suitable for the extraction of the light parts of Baku oil," which he tested under factory conditions. The American experience was also the inspiration for his next book, 304 pages long, *The Petroleum Industry in Pennsylvania and in the Caucasus,* in which he compared American and Russian progress in this industry.

He felt fine when he was through. Once again, work had rescued him from loneliness.

10

THE SORROW AND
HAPPINESS OF LOVE

In the spring of 1877, Mendeleyev's sister, Ekaterina, came to keep house for him in his St. Petersburg apartment. Feozva and little Olga were at Boblovo. Volodya, now twelve, was attending a maritime school in preparation for a naval career. Ekaterina brought her children and also a nineteen-year-old girl, Anna Ivanova Popov, who studied at the Academy of Art with Ekaterina's daughter, Nadezhda.

There was plenty of room for all of them. In the front part of the apartment, Mendeleyev had his bedroom, his combination study and laboratory, a hallway and a private entrance. The back rooms had a separate entrance. Except that his sister brought his meals and Nadezhda dropped in occasionally to chat with him, Mendeleyev might still have been living in solitude. Once or twice he caught a glimpse of a tall graceful girl with golden braids wound around her head, whom he judged to be the boarder of whom Ekaterina had spoken.

One morning as he was having breakfast he heard someone in the other part of the apartment playing Beethoven's Emperor Concerto on the piano.

"Who's playing?" he demanded when his sister came to clear away his table.

"It's Anna," his sister said. "I told her she might."

"The art student? She's musical too?"

"Yes." She stood with his tray. "Does her playing bother you? I'll have her stop if it does."

"I don't mind," Mendeleyev conceded. "I rather like it. She plays with strength and feeling, not like the usual woman parlor pianist."

For the next several days there was no music, at least when he was at home.

"What happened to her?" he brusquely asked his sister.

"To whom?" She looked puzzled.

"The art student. Why has she stopped playing?"

"Anna? I told her you liked to listen. Now she is afraid that she will make a mistake."

"You shouldn't have said anything to her," he burst out, glowering.

The next day he again had Beethoven with his breakfast. It was apparent his sister had informed the boarder that the master of the house wanted music.

The following Sunday he dined with his family for a change. Anna was at the table, and he had his first good look at her. Really lovely, he thought, with her golden hair, blue eyes, fair complexion and determined chin. Once she caught him looking at her, and her cheeks flushed to a rosy glow. She said almost nothing.

"Why is the art student so quiet?" he demanded of his sister afterward.

"I think you intimidate her," Ekaterina suggested mildly.

"I?" He was genuinely astonished. "But I have not said a word to her."

He was totally unaware that the whole household revolved around him, and knew nothing of the constant commands to the younger children to keep quiet when he slept or worked, of the search in the markets for his favorite foods, of the bustle and scurrying when it was time for his dinner or tea. All unknown to him, the youthful boarder had good reason to think that he must be some sort of ogre.

He began joining them regularly for their evening meal. One night after they had finished, Ekaterina suggested it might be nice if he and Anna played a game of chess together.

"You play chess?" he demanded, more gruffly than he had intended.

Anna nodded, blushing. "I used to play with my father."

"Good." He departed to his own room and brought back his chess box. Chess was his favorite relaxation, though usually when he had time for it there was no partner available.

Anna did not play badly, but he did not have to be a detective to note her nervousness. Obviously, she wished herself anywhere but where she was.

His mind was full of her when he went back to his study. What an unusual young woman, so talented and yet so modest! Instead of working, he sat down and wrote her a letter, pouring out his admiration. He did not dream of letting her see it. The letter went into a cedar box on his desk, which he kept locked.

Cleverly, or so he thought, he began to draw out his niece, Nadezhda, about their boarder.

From her he learned that Anna was the daughter of a retired doctor, Ivan Popov, who lived at Ourupenskoy Station in the Don Valley. Dr. Popov was progressive in his thinking and had wanted Anna to have a good education.

For five years she studied in a girl's boarding school in Moscow, directed by Countess Gorchakova, a relative of the writer Leo Tolstoy. In the fall of 1875, Anna had come to St. Petersburg to study music but later decided to take up drawing and sculpture at the Academy of Art, which Nadezhda was attending. The two girls had become friends, and Nadezhda had persuaded her mother to let Anna live with them.

Anna had more talent than anyone else at the academy, Nadezhda confided. Though she looked so feminine her painting was not limited to flowers and pretty landscapes. Her taste was for strong human figures, for mountain peaks and chasms, all ablaze with color. Would her uncle like to see them sometime?

"Yes," said Mendeleyev. "Yes, I think I would."

Anna was also a beautiful dancer, Nadezhda continued, obviously pleased at the chance to extol the virtues of her friend. At home they sometimes had parties. Carefully, she kept from her voice any note of reproach that since moving in with him, such affairs were banned. Once Anna had donned the costume of a nobleman's daughter and performed a well-known Russian dance. The artist Feodor Aleksandrovitch Feodorov, who was present, had been simply overwhelmed, saying that never, not even by professional dancers, had he seen a more expressive performance.

Did her uncle know that Anna had seen him even before they came to live with him?

"Saw me? Where? How?" he asked, bewildered.

"Last February. When you spoke at the University of St. Petersburg annual academic meeting. I took Anna with me and we sat in the back. She listened absolutely breathless throughout your lecture. Not until afterward did I tell her you were my uncle. She would not believe it. She said that, watching you, it was hard to imagine you had nieces and nephews like ordinary people."

Mendeleyev felt vaguely flattered, but even stronger was an indefinable sadness. He was a married man, growing old. He had no right, no right at all, to let his thoughts dwell on this young person. But he could not stop thinking of her.

More and more frequently he stopped for a chat in the room Nadezhda and Anna shared. Nadezhda's presence made these visits seem natural. She had always been close to her uncle and knew well that he was not as formidable as he was reputed to be.

Never before had he made such an effort to be entertaining. He talked about everything he thought might interest them, his childhood in Siberia, his days in Simferopol, Odessa and America. When he described how the Americans kept taking him for the Austrian monk Gregor Mendel, who "discovered heredity by growing green peas," both young women laughed merrily.

Once it was the girls who did all the talking, very excitedly. The Tsar Alexander II had paid a visit of inspection to the Academy of Art. They were frightened out of their wits, not only because he was the Tsar, but because, technically, the presence of women at the academy was illegal. But though the Tsar had seemed startled to see women students, he had made no comment. His silence meant that the ban was raised. Henceforth women were as free to study art as they were to attend Mendeleyev's chemistry classes or study medicine under Borodin.

Mendeleyev was still puzzled why women would want to study medicine and chemistry—obviously masculine subjects—but music and art were different. These were cultural pursuits, and Anna's mastery of them was part of the glamour she had for him. As she grew more at ease in his presence, he detected that beneath her modest manner was a gay and warm disposition and an even temper.

Night after night he wrote letters to her, letters increasingly filled with emotions hitherto foreign to him. Invariably he locked them in his cedar box. The box contained the secret of his heart. He had no intention that anyone should ever discover it.

One day he found Nadezhda alone in her room. Casually she told him that Anna had gone back to the Don Valley on a visit to her family.

"So?" He tried hard to hide his distress.

"She has a young man there," Nadezhda continued. "A young doctor—Vladimir Platonovitch Rubashkin. They will surely marry now that she has finished her studies. We shall probably not see her again. I'll miss her."

"Yes," he said slowly. "Yes, I imagine you will."

He turned and left the room.

But in the fall, Anna returned to St. Petersburg. Through Nadezhda, Mendeleyev learned that she had told Dr. Rubashkin that she could never accept the honor of being his wife, that she did not feel toward him as one should feel toward a companion for life.

The news made him happier than he dared admit. For a few days he had the joy of seeing her at his table again. Then Ekaterina told him she had decided to move her family back to her own apartment.

Did his sister guess his secret and wish to avoid trouble before it was too late? If so, her move was useless. Mendeleyev became a regular visitor at her home. Moreover he began holding socials at his apartment—something he had never done before. He invited, not his scientific friends, but outstanding musicians and artists and, of course, Anna and Nadezhda. Perhaps it would help them a little, he excused himself, to know these prominent people in their field.

One afternoon he found himself outside of the Academy of Art just as Anna was leaving. He almost believed what he told her, that it was a coincidence. There were other meetings, equally casual. In St. Petersburg's tightly knit intellectual circle, nothing Mendeleyev did was overlooked. There was gossip.

His head was in a whirl. He could not work and he could not sleep. In desperation he wrote to Anna's father, Dr. Popov, begging his permission to marry his daughter— if and when he could get a divorce. Dr. Popov came to see him, and humbly, because he knew Mendeleyev was a great man and a great scientist, begged him to leave his daughter alone. She was young. She could not know her own mind. Mendeleyev must see his viewpoint. After all he was a man of the world, married, with two children of his own.

The good doctor could not reproach him more than he reproached himself, but he was unable to stop seeing Anna. The letters were locked in his cedar box, but he could no longer put a lock on his tongue. He told her he loved her as he had never loved anybody, and said it so simply she could not doubt the truth of it. She is turn confided that the first time she had seen him—lecturing at the university —she had know him to be a man like no other in the world.

He went to Boblovo to see Feozva, who greeted him with her usual sad manner.

"I know why you have come," she said. "You don't need to say it. The answer is no. I won't and can't divorce you."

He told Anna of his visit.

She looked at him horrified. "How she must suffer!" she cried. "How unfair it is!"

Weeping, she followed her father's advice and went to Rome to study.

Mendeleyev lost weight, did not eat, went around half-sick.

In the midst of his despair came news that once would have caused him to explode with delight.

Sometime in 1879, a Swedish chemist, L. F. Nilson, discovered the spectrum of a new element in the rare mineral gadolinite. He named his find scandium, after Scandinavia. A fellow countryman, P. T. Cleve, analyzed this new substance. Before the end of the year, he announced that its properties were almost identical with those Mendeleyev had predicted for eka-boron.

His colleagues at the University gave a party in his honor.

"*Akh*, Dmitri Ivanovitch, it has happened again," they said, crowding around him. "The doubters are put to rest for good now. Do you know what the French are saying about you: 'Daring, more daring, always daring—that Mendeleyev!' And the Americans! In America they call you 'the world's greatest living chemist.'"

They thought that the tears running down his cheeks were shed from joy. To Menshutkin he confided the truth: "Without Anna, everything I have done or will ever do is meaningless."

"It takes time," Menshutkin tried to console him. "In time you will be healed." But even as he uttered the trite words, he was filled with doubts.

Mendeleyev's long-time friend and adviser, Nicolai Zinin, had died not long before. In his last years he had occupied the Chair of Chemical Technology at the Imperial Academy of Science, and now that place was vacant. The academy dated back to the time of Peter the Great, and in its charter was called the "leading scientific estate in the Russian Empire." Members were elected for life. On the death of a member, academicians were privileged to fill the vacancy with a scientist who in his work was "endeavoring to broaden the frontiers of any branch of knowledge useful to mankind and to improve and enrich it by his discoveries."

In all of Russia no one was more eligible for this high post than Mendeleyev. His candidacy was supported by Butelerov and other leading scientists. But unknown to them, there was strong opposition to him from certain quarters. The president of the academy, K. S. Veselouski, was jealous of the scientific developments at the University of St. Petersburg, for which Mendeleyev was largely responsible. Moreover, he was a close friend of the Minister of Education, Count Tolstoy, Mendeleyev's old enemy.

Tolstoy and Veselouski, working together, supported as their candidate a German Bavarian, Friedrich Konrad Beilstein. Beilstein, a professor at the Imperial Technological Institute, was a cold and sarcastic man, who stayed in Russia because to qualify as a professor in Germany he would have to do laboratory research, which he detested. Because of Tolstoy's influence, Beilstein, not Mendeleyev, was appointed to the vacant chair.

A wave of tremendous indignation swept the Russian scientific world. Nearly every scientist sent his own personal protest. All scientific bodies without exception expressed an adverse opinion to the decision.

Only Mendeleyev received the news in stony indifference. He could not have cared less. "It is a matter of no importance," he said.

Contrary to Menshutkin's wishful thinking, time had not cured his malady. Night and day his mind was filled with dreams of Anna. At times the dreams became hallucinations. Once he clearly heard the Emperor Concerto, as Anna had played it, in the next room. But when he dashed in, the piano was closed and covered with dust. His work suffered and he published nothing. His students could scarcely recognize this haggard listless man as their once vibrant and vigorous professor.

His colleagues shook their heads in despair. "At this rate, he will not live another year," one of them prophesied.

A group of them decided to take matters into their own hands. They went to see Feozva. At first she would not listen to them. Though she admittedly no longer lived with Mendeleyev as his wife, he was still her husband and the father of her children. To her, this Anna Popov was no better than a thief, trying to steal what was rightfully hers.

Mendeleyev's colleagues nodded with sympathy. They understood her feelings and agreed wholeheartedly that it was all very unfortunate. But she must know that Mendeleyev was not an ordinary man. He never did things halfway. With him it was all or nothing. That was one of the reasons for his greatness. It was also the reason his separation from this young person whom he loved was destroying him.

They told her about his perpetual gloom, his poor health, how he was neglecting his work.

"It is as bad as that?" she asked quietly.

Though their marriage had been so bungled, she did not hate him. And she was too conscientious to want to cause him harm.

A few days later she walked unannounced into his study.

"I have changed my mind, Dmitri Ivanovitch," she said steadily. "You can have a divorce."

In the astonished delight that swept through him, he hardly listened to the condition on which she would grant his freedom: that all his university salary be signed over to her and their two children. Without argument, he agreed. He still had his consultation fees and the royalties from *Principles of Chemistry* and his other writings. There would be enough, that is, if Anna did not mind comparative poverty.

Menshutkin saw him before he left for Rome to tell Anna the news.

"If she will not marry me, I will jump into the sea," he said.

He need not have worried. Anna's love was true and strong. The lack of money for their future life together made not the slightest difference to her.

"We will have each other," she told him wonderingly, as if there were no riches in the world to compare to that.

In January 1882, shortly after the divorce proceedings became final, they were married. For the first time, Mendeleyev learned the meaning of happiness.

11

ANNA'S FAMOUS HUSBAND

THE OFFICIAL RECOGNITION DENIED MENDELEYEV BY THE Imperial Academy of Science arrived from a foreign land.

He had been married only a few months when Anna waltzed into his study one morning, holding the letter on engraved stationery, emblazoned with foreign stamps.

He opened it and stared at it thoughtfully.

"Bad news, Mitenka?" she asked, calling him by her own favorite nickname.

"No," he said. "Not bad news. The Royal Society in London is giving me the Davy Medal for 1882."

"What is the Davy Medal?"

"It is named for Humphry Davy, a very great English scientist. He isolated the seven elements potassium, sodium, calcium, barium, boron, magnesium and strontium."

"Potassium, sodium, calcium, barium," she chanted. "It sounds like a poem."

"It does. Davy also invented a miner's lamp, whose flame would flare up to warn miners of seeping gas, yet would not ignite the gas. No one can say how many lives the Davy lamp has saved—or will save."

"What a marvelous invention! Tell me about it." Anna settled herself on a stool, a willing listener.

"An ingenious device," Mendeleyev said. "The wonder

is no one thought of it before. He surrounded the flame with a metal gauze. Gas could pass through the metal and make the flame burn more brightly, but the fire could not pass the wire barrier."

"And this wonderful Professor Davy has given you a medal?" demanded Anna, bringing him back to the point.

"Indirectly," he explained. "The miners gave Davy a lot of silver plate to show their gratitude. When he died, he left a will donating the silver to the Royal Society, with the request that it be made into medals and that one be given each year for an outstanding scientific discovery. This year it is for the Periodic Law. I get a medal and so does Lothar Meyer."

"Lothar Meyer? Who is he?"

"A German. An excellent chemist. He too made a Periodic Table."

Her face fell. "I thought it was your discovery. Yours alone."

"That is not quite so. Others had the same idea as I, though Meyer came closer to the truth than the others. In science, people often work on the same problems and make the same discoveries, even knowing nothing of each other's work." He added with almost childlike pride. "But Meyer did not forecast the properties of unknown elements nor risk changing atomic weights. That was why my table was the best."

"How vain you are!" She jumped up and clasped her arms around his neck. "How very vain!"

When the Davy Medal arrived, Mendeleyev gave it to Anna and forgot about it. She put it in the small cedar chest he had turned over to her at the time of their marriage—the chest holding all the love letters he had written and never mailed.

Since his marriage, he was different and his life was different. Where gloom had ruled, now there was gaiety. Often he broke out singing, for no reason at all. Friends flocked to their home. Twice a week, on Wednesday and Friday, they held informal parties. Their guests were a mixture of artists and musicians, chemists and physicists.

Art galleries sent their publications so they could be discussed in the Mendeleyev home. Sometimes the artists themselves brought a new painting for the opinion of the guests and hosts. Mendeleyev himself became passionately interested in art. One of their friends, the artist Arkhip Ivanovitch Koundzhi, exhibited his "A Night in the Ukraine." For the newspaper *The Voice,* Mendeleyev wrote an article about it called "Before a Picture by Koundzhi," in which he interpreted the painting as a transition from self-contemplation to the love of nature. Because of his artistic understanding, the Academy of Art (in 1894) elected him a member. This pleased him as much as any scientific honor he ever received.

Another artist friend was Nicolai Alexandrovitch Yaroshenko. Often Anna visited him and his wife at their studio home in the Chinese section of town. Half-joking, Yaroshenko promised to paint the portrait of her first child.

The first child of Anna and Mendeleyev was born late in 1882, a beautiful blond girl. They called her Liubov, which means "love." The next year there was a boy they named Ivan.

Mendeleyev had tried to conceal from his young wife his one regret—the enforced separation from Olga and Volodya. She was too sensitive to his moods not to guess how he felt. Liubov and Ivan were her gifts to him, to help make up for his loss.

In 1884, he was invited to Scotland to receive the honorary degree of Doctor of Law from the University of Edinburgh. There in 1869, Thomas Andrews, the Irish chemist, had published his papers on "critical temperatures," about the same phenomenon that Mendeleyev previously at Heidelberg had called "absolute boiling point." In presenting him with the honorary degree, the university was belatedly giving Mendeleyev credit for his share in this important discovery.

Because of the children, Anna could not go with him. He went because Anna insisted she would not let him miss it for anything; that he had to go so he could tell her all about it. It was their first separation since their marriage.

After the ceremonies at Edinburgh, Mendeleyev went to London, where he was invited to attend a dinner in honor of William Henry Perkin, the discoverer of the first artificial dye. He arrived early at the hotel where the dinner was to be held. Only one other guest was there, an elegant young man with a goatee. Mendeleyev politely bowed to him.

"I think we should have a good attendance tonight," the stranger said in English.

Mendeleyev's stay in America had not made him any more proficient in that language.

"I do not speak English," he explained.

"*Vielleicht sprechen sie deutsch?*" asked the stranger. ("Perhaps you speak German?")

"*Ja,*" Mendeleyev told him. "*Ein wenig. Ich bin Mendeleyev.*" ("Yes, a bit. I am Mendeleyev.")

The Englishman, who did not seem to know him, said his name was Ramsay, which was equally unfamiliar to Mendeleyev. In German, they managed to keep up a conversation for about twenty minutes until the other guests showed up.

In his memoirs, Sir William Ramsay described Mendeleyev as "a peculiar foreigner, every hair of whose head acted in independence of every other." He continued, "He is a nice sort of fellow, but his German is not perfect. He said he was raised in East Siberia and knew no Russian until he was seventeen years old. I suppose he is a Kalmuck or one of those outlandish creatures."

There was justice in Ramsay's remark about his hair. Mendeleyev permitted his hair and beard to be cut only once a year, in the spring. By winter both were so long and thick that he resembled his Slavic ancestors in the days before Peter the Great decided that Russian gentlemen must groom themselves in the manner of the western Europeans.

Happily unaware that the English had found him such an "outlandish creature," Mendeleyev returned to Russia soon after the banquet. Not any scientific enticement in the world could have kept him away longer.

With his marriage, contentment had replaced yearning. Otherwise the pattern of his days changed little. Work was as necessary to him as food and air. On days when he had no lectures, he was at his desk from early in the morning until half-past five. Dinner was at six. If they had no guests, he returned to his study and worked until late at night. Anna did not protest these long hours. She had known this was the way it would be.

Oil production still interested him deeply, and he continued to write articles about it—about his proposed pipeline from Baku to Batum on the Black Sea, about the best methods to refine crude naphtha, about other steps that must be taken if Russia was to prosper from her underground wealth. After years of dilly-dallying, the government and the industrial leaders were beginning to heed his advice. The pipeline was built. Reforms in leasing laws were made. Russia became the second oil-producing country in the world, surpassed only by the United States and offering serious competition to America in oil exports.

Whatever satisfaction Mendeleyev felt must have been tinted with disillusion. For all the new wealth pouring into Russia, the common people profited little. Alexander III, who succeeded his father, assassinated in 1881, blindly and stubbornly pursued the course of dictatorial rule that had brought disaster to his father. Talk of a constitutional monarchy was abhorrent to him; he called a parliament "an institution for the satisfaction of personal ambitions." In an open letter to him, a group called "The People's Will" pleaded for freedom of speech, of the press and of public assembly. The Tsar ignored it. Minority groups, especially the Jews and the Poles, were the victims of increased persecution.

Count Tolstoy, Minister of Education, became President of the Imperial Academy of Science in 1882. When he knew he was going to die, he summoned Veselouski, the former president. "Only remember," he said, "Mendeleyev must not be recognized by the academy in any way." But even this petty vengeful gesture could not dam up the mounting torrent of acclaim for the man who had put the elements in order.

Since the discovery of scandium in 1875, scientists throughout the world were on the lookout for more of Mendeleyev's predicted elements, particularly eka-silicon, which he had described in great detail, even to its gray color and the kind of ore in which it would be found.

Among the investigators was a German chemist, C. A. Winkler, who had made a careful study of Mendeleyev's writings about the periodic law and the relationship of the "chemical elements." From the rare silver ore argyrodite, Winkler extracted, in 1885, a grayish substance which yielded an unfamiliar spectrum. He guessed at once that it might be eka-silicon and proceeded with great haste to its analysis.

Mendeleyev had prophesied that eka-silicon would have an atomic weight of 72, that its specific gravity would be 5.5 and that its salts would easily dissolve in water. Winkler found his new element to have an atomic weight of 72.3 and a specific gravity of 5.35. Its salts dissolved easily in water, and its other properties also closely matched Mendeleyev's description.

"There is no doubt that this is Mendeleyev's 'eka-silicon,'" Winkler wrote in his report. "The correspondence is remarkable. . . . I doubt whether there could be a clearer proof of the correctness of the theory of the periodicity of elements. It is more than a simple affirmation of the daring theory. It signifies an outstanding broadening of our chemical horizon, a gigantic step forward in the field of knowledge."

As De Boisbaudran and Nilson had done, Winkler named his element after his native land. Germanium, he called it.

Mendeleyev's own delight in the discovery of germanium was surpassed only by the birth of twins in 1886, a little girl named Maria for Mendeleyev's mother, and a boy, Vassili, for the uncle who had turned over his glass factory to their family.

The verification of eka-silicon created an upheaval and a sensation, by far exceeding the discovery of gallium and scandium. Throughout Europe and America scientists could talk of nothing else. Of the six predictions Mendeleyev had made, three had been found within sixteen years. No one doubted now that the other three would turn up eventually.

No one doubted either that the periodic table was a "law of nature," as Mendeleyev had long claimed. The news reached Sir William Ramsay, now a professor at University College, London. "Our teacher, Mendeleyev," he henceforth called the "peculiar foreigner" from Siberia.

The excitement even penetrated the Winter Palace and the ears of the autocratic Alexander III.

An Imperial messenger, foppishly clad in knee breeches and livery, rang the knocker on the door of Mendeleyev's apartment. Anna, frightened and impressed, brought him into her husband's study.

"His Highest and Most Exalted Majesty requests the Professor Dmitri Ivanovitch Mendeleyev at the court," the messenger read from a long document.

"The Tsar wants to see me?" interrupted Mendeleyev. "Whatever for?"

"I do not know," the man said. "But is a great honor."

Mendeleyev deliberated a long moment. "Tell the Tsar I will be there and on time," he said.

All during the interview Anna had stood motionless as a statue, her eyes sparkling. As the door closed behind their visitor, this mother of four clapped her hands together as delightedly as a child.

"Imagine, Mitenka. You are going to see the Tsar. I know he is not intelligent like you. He is not even a good man. Still, it is something. When I was a little girl I used to dream of attending a ball in the Tsar's palace. What a foolish dream!"

"For a woman—not a foolish dream," he told her fondly. "For myself, I'd rather stay here. It is a waste of time."

"Perhaps you should buy a new frock coat," she suggested.

"What? Throw our money away like that? Never!" he said.

She knew better than to press him. "If you would at least have your hair and beard trimmed a little . . ."

He looked at her in stunned surprise. "No, I could not do that either. The Tsar must see me as I am."

His colleagues heard of the Imperial summons.

"Perhaps, Dmitri Ivanovitch, you ought to cut your hair and beard before you appear in court."

"I will not," he said.

Nor could anyone change his mind.

"You will tell me what it is like—the Winter Palace," Anna pleaded before he left. "You will remember everything?"

"I will do my best," he promised.

The four small children were long asleep when he returned, but Anna was waiting for him, eagerly and anxiously. She half-expected that the brush with Imperial splendor would leave its mark on him, but there was no change. Her husband was the same as when he had left, a tall, slightly stooped man, in a long greatcoat, with a great beard, long unkempt hair and kind blue eyes.

He kissed her with unusual tenderness. "My tea, Anna, is it ready?"

"Yes, Mitenka." She poured the brew from the samovar, adding sugar and lemon.

"Good." He took a deep draught. "All the way home I have been thinking how much I needed a glass of tea."

Another digression? This time she would not permit it.

"And the Tsar?" she burst out. "How was he?"

"He seemed in good health," he said. "As far as I could judge. A big husky healthy man."

"Is that all you can tell me?"

"Why no. We had a nice chat."

"About what?"

"About gallium, scandium and germanium. He wanted to know why none of these had been named after Russia, since I was the one who predicted them. I told him that in science there was an agreement that anyone who found a new element could name it whatever he wished. He did not seem too pleased. He asked me why no new elements had been discovered in Russia, and I said there was no order in how elements were found, though the elements themselves were very orderly."

"You are making things up, Mitenka," Anna cried. "You would not have said such a thing to the Tsar."

"I think he wanted me to find an element, so I could name it alexandrium after him," Mendeleyev continued, his face impassive. "Of course, I would not do that. I would call it annium, for you."

She burst out laughing.

"And the palace? What was it like? Or didn't you notice?"

"I promised you I would, did I not?" he asked reproachfully. "I noticed everything. They had me wait in a great hall lined with marble colonnades. I have never seen so many kinds of marble in one place—red, gold veined with rose, and sulfur yellow, the latter mined in the Urals, I believe. On the walls were mirrors reaching to the ceiling. What a remarkable silvering job! I could not see a single flaw. There were also some tremendous vases of dark green malachite set on pilasters. It must have been mined in Russia too. Nowhere else in Europe can you find such beautiful malachite. Other vases, smaller ones, were of lapis lazuli. If I remember correctly, Peter the Great had the lapis lazuli brought from Afghanistan. You would have liked the chandeliers. They were hung with crystals and blazing with hundreds of candles. There! Could anyone have been more observant than I?"

"You did splendidly, Mitenka," she said, giggling helplessly. "A scientist has eyes to see what others miss. Now tell me about the people. Is it true that the court ladies wear velvet gowns with ermine trains and so many sapphires and other jewels on their headdresses that they can hardly bear the weight?"

"I am sorry, Anna," he confessed, shamefacedly. "I did not pay any attention to the women."

12

THE BUBBLE THAT
PIERCED THE SKY

ON AUGUST 7, 1887, RUSSIA WOULD BE THE SETTING FOR A total eclipse. Long in advance astronomers had notified the world of this forthcoming event. On that day, across a belt 140 miles wide, from the Baltic Sea to the Sea of Japan, the earth's small moon would briefly blot out the huge and blazing sun.

This phenomenon was of special interest to science. While the eclipse was at its total phase, the brilliant flames which leap up thousands of miles above the sun's surface would be briefly visible and could be studied as they could not on a normal sunny day.

For the past three years all Russian scientific organizations, including the Russian Chemical Society, had been working together in planning for the eclipse. A temporary observatory was built, and in addition observers were assigned to specific posts all along the broad band of the eclipse's path. Appeals were made to ordinary citizens to be on the alert that day, to make sketches and send in any unusual information. As the time grew near, astronomers and other scientists arrived from France, Germany, Italy,

England and the United States, to take their recordings alongside their Russian colleagues.

Mendeleyev, like everyone else, was caught up in the excitement. How could it be otherwise? It was during the total eclipse of 1868 in India that helium had been identified, the enigmatic element that still had not been found on earth. There was a close bond between chemistry and astronomy, as there was with all the sciences.

Although he had acted as adviser in the preparations, he made no plans to participate himself. He was spending the summer at Boblovo with Anna and the children. Agricultural experiments occupied much of his time. Because one activity alone was never enough, he was working on alcohol solutions again, on the density and structure of sulfuric acid solutions, and on an analysis of certain meteorites.

A week before the eclipse a telegram arrived from M. N. Ghersevanov, president of the Russian Technological Society. It said tersely that the society had just succeeded in getting a balloon for the study of the eclipse. A trained aeronaut, Lieutenant Kovanko, would man the balloon. They needed a scientist to go with him and handle the measuring instruments. Would Mendeleyev accept?

Still holding the telegram, Mendeleyev went to the open window of his study and gazed across the green fields. Exuberance filled his spirit. What an adventure to sail through the "ocean of air," which he still foresaw would one day become as much a part of transportation as the "oceans of water." What a splendid opportunity was being handed to him! To his knowledge no one before him had viewed a solar eclipse from the height to which a balloon could safely rise.

The word "safely" gave him pause. The balloon he had designed in 1875 with the hermetically sealed gondola, in which the pilot could breathe "compressed air," was still unbuilt. The century since men had taken to the air had been marred with a number of catastrophes. The only lighter-than-air substance yet found to inflate balloons was highly inflammable hydrogen. Fresh in everyone's mind was the tragedy of the *Zenith,* which had taken three French scientists aloft to the height of 29,000 feet. Only one had returned alive; the other two had quite literally frozen to death.

The tang of danger did not affect his decision to go one way or another, but one thing bothered him. How was he going to tell Anna? She must be made to understand the benefit to science of his trip. He must approach the matter carefully, with diplomacy, not to frighten her.

He went downstairs and out on the porch. Anna and Nadezhda, who was visiting them, had taken their easels, paints and brushes out on the wide lawn beneath a spreading beech tree. Beside them the twins were sleeping in their baby carriage, while Liubov and Ivan were tumbling over each other in a game of leapfrog.

What a pretty sight, he thought. For several moments, unnoticed, he stood watching the scene, the two young women, one dark and one fair, and the romping children, all against a background of varied greens and shade and sunlight.

"*Papachka!*" Liubov, who was nearly five now, had spied him and ran toward him, her chubby arms outstretched.

He stepped down from the porch and caught her in his arms.

"You want to know something, my little lovebird," he fairly shouted. "Your *papachka* is going up in the air in a balloon! Way up in the air like this!" He lifted her high above his head until she squealed with joy.

Then he saw Anna and Nadezhda staring at him in consternation.

"Is it truly safe, Mitenka?" asked Anna for the sixteenth time, later that night when he had told her all the things about the flight that he had intended to tell her before his abrupt announcement.

"Perfectly safe," he lied brazenly.

Nonetheless in the next few days he made out his will and sent for Volodya and Olga, his two oldest children whom he saw so rarely. Olga was nineteen now, a quiet young woman with large thoughtful eyes, already engaged to be married. Her brother, in his Marine Corps uniform, was a handsome youth of twenty-two. Their faces were solemn and concerned when he told them what he was going to do.

"Where is the flight to be, Father?" Volodya asked.

"At Klin. A small town thirty-one miles northwest of Moscow, right in the band of the eclipse. The total phase will start at six forty-five in the morning and last one hundred and fifty seconds."

"I will go on ahead and make sure everything is properly prepared," Volodya volunteered. "That is, if you do not object."

"I do not object," Mendeleyev assured him. "I shall be proud and glad."

In the privacy of his study he practiced over and over again the series of recordings and measurements he planned to make with the barometer he had invented, his thermometer and other instruments. With so little time to work, not a single gesture could be wasted. All his spare time he spent with Anna and the children. Never had they seemed so dear to him.

"You are to stay here and not worry," he told Anna firmly before he left Boblovo.

Instead of answering, she threw her arms around his neck and held him close.

He and his tall son, Volodya, spent the night before the eclipse as guests of the mayor of Klin. The ascent was scheduled for six the next morning. Mendeleyev, with his son and the mayor, arrived at the town square, the scene of the take-off, before five. Hundreds of spectators were already there, townspeople, peasants come in from their farms, distinguished visitors from Moscow and St. Petersburg and, although Mendeleyev did not know it, Nadezhda and Anna. They had both been much too upset and thrilled to stay home as he had instructed them to do. So he would not recognize them, they wore veils over their faces.

The sky was gray and overcast—an ominous sign. Everyone stood silently awaiting the miracle. A guard moved ahead, clearing a path for Mendeleyev and his party. Suddenly a woman's voice rang out.

"There he is! The man who is going to pierce the sky with a bubble!"

An awed murmur spread through the crowd.

In the center of the square was the great yellow balloon, stirring and swelling like some prehistoric monster as hydrogen was being pumped into it. The mayor introduced Lieutenant Kovanko, the aeronaut, a serious intent young man who was supervising the proceedings. He and Mendeleyev shook hands.

"What a pity about the weather," the lieutenant said. "What a pity that a few clouds could destroy all this planning."

Mendeleyev squinted up at the sky. "It is too soon to lose hope. Perhaps it will clear."

They waited until the balloon was swollen full size, its sides slick and smooth. Kovanko and Mendeleyev climbed into the gondola beneath it. Mendeleyev arranged his instruments so they would be within easy reach. Already the sky was beginning to darken.

"Cut the ropes!" the lieutenant called to his men.

They did so. The balloon swayed slightly but did not rise.

"The dew," diagnosed Mendeleyev, frowning. "It soaked up too much dew overnight."

One after another they tossed out their sandbags, all but two, which they had to keep so that later on they could control the descent. Still the balloon did not move.

It was becoming more like night every second.

"There is only one solution, lieutenant," Mendeleyev said. "I will go alone."

"Impossible, sir," snapped Kovanko. "The War Ministry has ordered me to escort you. I cannot disobey orders."

In seven more minutes the eclipse would be total.

"Get out," roared Mendeleyev. "Get out or I will throw you out. Tell the War Ministry that. No one is going to keep me from meeting the eclipse!"

The lieutenant saluted and obeyed him. At once the balloon began to rise. In kindly fashion, Mendeleyev waved to his escort from the gondola.

Anna, whitefaced, turned to Nadezhda and Volodya. "He is going alone. Knowing nothing of the controls. Oh, my darling!" Weeping, she watched until the balloon vanished in the dark skies.

Far above Klin, working in almost complete darkness, Mendeleyev was using barometer and thermometer to take altitude and temperature readings. Then a real miracle happened. The clouds parted, revealing the black disc of the moon surrounded by a silver ring—the corona. It was wider on one side than on the other, he noted. As he watched, flaming red protuberances shot out beyond the corona. This was the solar crown, visible only during a total eclipse. He kept his eyes fixed on the spectacle for fifteen seconds before a thin and wayward cloud floated past, dimming the image. Immediately afterward a larger cloud blotted out everything.

His disappointment was keen. The clouds in the sky were still beyond the control of science. That quick clear view of the darting red flames was in itself worth the time and risk. Like a small piece in a jigsaw puzzle, it might help solve the mystery of the sun's seemingly boundless energy. A mystery that he had no doubt would one day be unraveled in full.

He continued to take his readings, knowing that these would be less valuable than those made before the clouds shut away the eclipse. For a while the temperature rose, then fell, then rose again. He concluded this must be due to the variation of the cloud distribution. In this eerie world of mist and twilight, he was terrifyingly alone, yet it did not occur to him to be afraid. When the balloon reached a height of 11,375 feet, he felt it was time for the descent.

Though it was true he had never handled the controls of a balloon, he knew in principle what to do. Tied to the gondola was a rope which hung from a valve in the side of the balloon. Mendeleyev pulled on it, thus opening the valve so that the hydrogen gas could seep out. At once the balloon began to descend, much too rapidly. He released the rope and tossed over a bag of sand. The balloon steadied itself. A gust of wind caught up his floating ship and swept it along at a fast pace. Clearly, wherever he landed, it would not be at Klin.

In the ascent, after the take-off, there were no serious

problems. To make it come down, gently, surely, and not too quickly, was a matter of skill and patience. Practice would have helped too, but that he lacked.

A frown creased his high forehead, as he again pulled the rope, then let go of it. The trick, he realized, was to let the gas out just a little at a time, so that he would glide, not drop to the earth so frighteningly far beneath him. Over and over he tugged at the rope, then released it. The skies were still sultry but daylight had returned. The eclipse was over.

He had been in the air only two hours, but it seemed longer. Everything was under control. The monstrous creature that had carried him so faithfully was proving obedient to his every command. What a wonderful feeling! He wanted to shout to the whole world that he had mastered the air. At the moment of his greatest self-confidence, he was caught off-guard. All of a sudden the dark green forest below rushed up toward him. Just in time he threw the remaining half sack of sand overboard. The balloon scuttled upward, barely missing the tops of the tallest trees.

Beyond the forest he skimmed over a bright green meadow. Once more he pulled on the rope, as hard as he could. The balloon, shrunk to half its former size, balked, like a skittish mare. Beneath him, there was shouting and some muzhiks came running in his direction.

"Look!" someone called. "A man has sailed from the sky in a comet!" Already that day they had seen dawn turn to night. Now they were faced with an equally incredible sight.

He threw them a rope which he had found coiled in a corner and which had one end securely fastened to the gondola.

"Grab it and hold on, little brothers!"

A muzhik seized it, hauled on it with all his strength, and

finally managed to tie it to a tree. The gondola settled on
solid ground. It was 9:00 A.M. Mendeleyev climbed stiffly
out to greet his wondering rescuers.

He was in the province of Tver, he learned, some one
hundred and fifty miles from Klin. Later, from a nearby
village, he sent two telegrams, one to Klin's mayor and one
to his wife. He reached Klin the next morning, accompanied
by Volodya, who had met him in Moscow. The crowd at
the station was much larger than the one that had watched
him leave. As he stepped from the train, an enormous cheer
resounded.

A troika was waiting for them. Some young men tried
to unharness the horses so they could have the honor of
dragging the vehicle that carried the scientist through the
village streets.

"I will not have it," bellowed Mendeleyev. "I thank you,
but no man is going to strain his back for me."

The mayor, sitting with them in the troika, was beside
himself with joy. "Today Klin is the most famous city in
Russia," he boasted, as though the town, not Mendeleyev,
was responsible for the balloon's successful flight. In detail
he described the festivities that were being arranged.

But Mendeleyev would not stay for them. He had pierced
the sky with a bubble and come back to the green earth
riding a comet, but now all he wanted was to get home.
The troika rode slowly through the town, amidst the shouting, cheering populace. He said good-by to the mayor and
thanked him for his hospitality. The driver stopped long
enough to leave him at his door and then, on Mendeleyev's
instructions, turned his horses into the open road which led
to Boblovo

"Oh, Mitenka," Anna sobbed in his arms that night.
"Don't ever go so far and so high again."

13

THE RESIGNATION

St. Petersburg slept, its dark wide streets silent and empty.

In his study Mendeleyev sat under his sputtering oil lamp before a mammoth stack of closely written papers. Another work was added to the many others, a manuscript over 500 pages called *Investigation of Aqueous Solutions by Means of Specific Gravity*. Ever since his triumphal ascent to the skies, and even before, he had been working on it. His eyes burned and fatigue pierced his brain and body. No matter. Nothing could dull the glow of a job well done.

"You are my favorite, Mitya. Perhaps I should not say it but it is true. I have always known you would go further than the others."

His mother's words came sharply out of the past. Suddenly he saw her, as clearly as though it were yesterday, sitting erect and proud in the driver's seat of the telega that had brought them to Moscow, her dark hair coiled around her head and her eyes looking straight ahead into his future.

"*Akh*, little mother," he murmured. "You asked so much of me."

The door of his study opened quietly. His beautiful

wife, clad in her dressing robe with her golden hair hanging in two long braids, stood in the doorway.

"How is the book coming, Mitenka?"

"Done," he told her. "Tomorrow we celebrate."

"Wonderful!" she cried. "You are coming to bed now?"

"In a few minutes. There is one thing to add."

With the intuition that was part of her nature, she vanished.

Alone again, he took out another sheet of paper and printed at the top, "Preface."

"This research," he wrote, "is dedicated to the memory of a mother by her youngest offspring. Conducting a factory, she could educate him only by her own work. She instructed by example, corrected with love, and in order to give him to the cause of science she left Siberia with him, spending thus her last resources and strength.

"When dying, she said, 'Be careful of illusions. Work. Search for divine and scientific truth . . .' She understood how often arguments deceive, how much there is still to be learned, and how, with the help of science, without violence, with love but firmness, all superstition, untruth, and error are removed, bringing in their place the safety of discovered truth, freedom for further development, general welfare, and inward happiness. Dmitri Mendeleyev regards as sacred a mother's dying words."

He laid down his pen and turned out the lamp. Now he could get the rest he needed.

In the spring of 1888, the Ministry of State Property asked Mendeleyev to go to the coal mining region in the Donets Basin. They wanted him to do for coal what he had done for the oil industry. He agreed at once, glad of another chance to use scientific knowledge for his country's benefit.

On his return from the long journey, he wrote a series of articles outlining recommendations on what could be done to make coal mining more efficient. One of his suggestions was to build canals from the coal fields to the Don and its tributaries, so that coal could economically be shipped by water to the manufacturing centers.

He made another trip the next year, and this time Anna went with him. England had granted him a double tribute. The Royal Society invited him to address one of their meetings, and the British Chemical Society wanted him to deliver their annual Faraday lecture, named after the great English scientist, Michael Faraday. No Russian scientist had ever been so honored. "Madame Mendeleyev" was included in the invitations. Nadezhda agreed to stay at Boblovo and look after the children in their absence.

"You never took time for a honeymoon. Now is your chance. Enjoy yourself and worry about nothing," she told them.

In Paris, where they stopped for a few days, Mendeleyev bought his wife an evening gown, the most beautiful, and most expensive, she had ever owned.

"I understand that in London, scientific lectures are a social affair," he explained, half-apologetically. "Women dress to the hilt. I want you to outshine them all."

The crossing on the Channel was stormy, and Anna was desperately sick. Solid and stately London soon restored her equilibrium. A sensational welcome was waiting for them from the scientists of England.

No longer could even the most skeptical dismiss the periodic law as interesting but not wholly original. Not only had three elements been found to match Mendeleyev's descriptions of eka-boron, eka-aluminum and eka-silicon, but one by one his bold changes of accepted atomic weights

were also being accepted, even including his drastic altera-
tion of the atomic weight of uranium from 120 to 240. For
other chemists, finding an atomic weight of an element was
a mathematical and chemical problem involving infinite
pains. Mendeleyev alone performed the feat from theory
and deduction. No wonder he was called a magician.

A young Russian-speaking professor was assigned to look
after them.

"Would you like to know what our scientists are saying
about your husband?" he asked Anna.

"Yes, I would."

"They are saying that he is for Russia what Dumas was
for France, what Berzelius was for Sweden, and what Liebig
was for Germany," he told her, as though no greater tribute
could be paid to any man.

She did not know who these other scientists were, but
was convinced that Mitenka surpassed them all.

Mendeleyev's first lecture was the one for the Royal
Society, held at London's Royal Institution on May 31,
1889. Sir Frederick Abel, the Royal Society president,
greeted them on their arrival and presented them to some
of the illustrious guests. This time Anna had made her husband coach her in advance, so she would be able to associate
their names with their work.

One of them was Sir Edward Frankland, author of the
theory of valency, which had to do with the number of
atoms certain elements demanded of other elements to
unite with their atoms and form compounds. The similar
elements in Mendeleyev's periodic system had the same
valency. Another guest was J. A. R. Newland, whose law
of octaves had been a forerunner of the periodic table. Once
people had laughed at his work, but now he, like Mendeleyev,
had been awarded the Davy Medal.

She also met Dr. Ludwig Mond, president of the Chemical-Technical Society, Sir Frederic Bramwell, president of the British Association, Sir William Crookes, discoverer of thallium, Sir James Dewar, who had liquefied oxygen, and so many others that her head was swimming.

Most of these gentlemen had brought their wives, which meant more names and faces to remember, and she observed that though quite a few were bedecked with the most gorgeous jewels and wraps, none had a prettier evening gown than the one her husband had bought for her.

"I am pleased to meet you." She repeated this memorized English formula over and over. When the English replied in long and obvious flattering phrases, she could only nod and smile, understanding nothing.

Finally they all were gathered in the assembly hall. On the platform next to Mendeleyev stood Sir James Dewar, who read the English version of his lecture. It was called "An Attempt to Apply to Chemistry One of the Principles of Newton's Natural Philosophy," and its theme was the interrelation of physics and chemistry.

Anna, in her becoming French gown, sat opposite the platform, her eyes not on the speaker but on her husband.

For the first time in his life he was wearing a tuxedo. Their professor-guide had suggested it, and Anna coaxed him into it, over his violent protests. Tuxedos were for aristocrats, he argued, not for him. Even for the Tsar himself he had not changed his style of dress. He yielded only when Anna hinted that the English might consider it an affront to their hospitality if he appeared in his usual gray jacket. Even so, he insisted on wearing his Russian boots.

How splendid he looked in his tuxedo and Russian boots, with his mighty beard and strong features! It seemed to Anna that everyone in the room must be aware of his superiority to other men. When Dewar finished reading, she joined in the thunderous applause.

During the next day or so they were entertained by more scientists, including Sir William Ramsay, whom Anna's husband had met on his first trip to England. It was a pleasure to see the reverent way Sir William treated him, as though he were the wisest man in the world. There were indeed so many invitations that to accept them all they would have had to be in six places at the same time. But then they had to cancel everything.

The Faraday lecture was scheduled for June 4. Two days earlier a telegram came from Nadezhda in Boblovo. "Vassili seriously ill with abscess on left lung. Wire permission for emergency operation."

A telegram authorizing the operation was sent at once. An hour later, their clothes thrown hastily into their suitcases, the two were on their way home. Neither remembered clearly afterward the nightmare journey, by boat, train and, from Moscow, by troika. It was night when they reached Boblovo. All the lights were burning brightly. Mendeleyev, not even waiting for the driver to stop, jumped out and raced for the house, Anna close behind him.

Katerina, their servant, had heard them and was holding the door open.

"The little one lives," she whispered. "The doctor who operated says he will get well."

"God is good," breathed Mendeleyev, crossing himself.

Nadezhda, pale and drawn, came unsteadily down the stairs. Then she and Anna were in each other's arms, weeping with joy and relief.

In London, the English translation of Mendeleyev's Faraday lecture for the British Chemical Society was read in his absence. Later he received by mail the Faraday Medal, which was to have been awarded him personally. There were also joint gifts from the Royal Society and the Chemical Society, for Anna two vases inscribed with her initials, and for her husband, a goblet of aluminum and gold. By this time little Vassili was on the road to complete recovery.

Count Tolstoy had been replaced as Minister of Education by Count I. D. Delyanov, whose repressive measures exceeded those of his predecessor. "Minister of noneducation," the students called him behind his back.

In line with the growing rise of anti-Semitism, the quota for Jewish students was set as low as three per cent at some universities, depriving thousands of them from any schooling beyond the primary level. Delyanov was equally oppose to education for women. The Women's Medical College, started by Alexandre Borodin with such high hopes, was closed down. Only because of Mendeleyev's great prestige was he allowed to continue his chemistry classes for women.

To keep high schools and universities safe from "children of coachmen, footmen, laundresses, small shopkeepers," and others of the "lower classes," government scholarships, such as the one that had permitted Mendeleyev his education, were cut to the minimum, and tuition fees were raised for everyone. Students of poor families who still insisted on learning had to work at whatever wretched jobs they could find to pay their way. They lived crowded four or five in an unheated room, and were underfed, shabby and often too weak and exhausted to study.

Mendeleyev was furious. For years he had called himself "an evolutionist of a peaceful type." Though he sometimes used his influence to help certain of his more ardent students who were in trouble, so far as was possible he had avoided politics, hoping that in time conditions would improve. Instead they were worsening.

"It is compounded idiocy!" he exploded to Anna in the privacy of their home. The future of Russia depended on the intelligence and wisdom of her young people. Could there be any greater folly than to deprive them of their right to learn?

All that winter of 1889 and 1890 he sensed the undercurrent of rebellion.

One windy day in early March as he stepped out of the university buildings, his way was blocked by a crowd of student demonstrators, just as it had been once before when he was a freshman, newly enrolled in the Pedagogical Institute.

"Give us freedom," read their placards. "Economic support for students!" "Decrease the matriculation fee!"

He could not blame them. Not now. The wonder was that their demands were so mild.

Suddenly he heard his name.

"Mendeleyev! Mendeleyev!" The call was taken up by others. "We need you, Dmitri Ivanovitch."

"I'm a teacher," he told them. "I can tell you about chemistry. What more do you want of me?"

"We want to know how you feel," spoke up one of the youths.

"I feel you should study," he told them. "You are here to learn."

"We can't study. We are hungry."

"I would like to help but there is nothing I can do." He turned away, cursing to himself at his own helplessness.

Later that afternoon one of his chemistry students, a slender eager youth with eyes burning darkly in his white face, came to his apartment. Anna brought him into the study. There was nothing unusual in such a visit. Students were always dropping in to ask about their work, knowing that Mendeleyev never refused time or advice. But this youth had not come about his studies.

"On March 14 we are holding a meeting," he said. "To discuss the intolerable situation of the students. Several professors are invited. Will you come, Dmitri Ivanovitch?"

"It would serve no purpose," Mendeleyev told him.

Nonetheless, at the appointed time, he climbed up the rickety stairs to the dimly lit and shabby hall where the meeting was held. Crowds of young people were milling around, and he entered, he thought, unnoticed.

The meeting came to order. The student chairman read a petition of grievances prepared by a student committee and addressed to I. D. Delyanov. It was accepted by unanimous vote.

"The question before us now is who should present it to the Minister," said the chairman. "The floor is open for discussion."

A hand shot up and a youth jumped to his feet. "We all know it is useless for any of us to take the petition. It would only go in the wastebasket, like all the others. To be effective, it must be presented by a person of importance, whom Delyanov will not dare ignore. I suggest we find such a person."

Several hands were waving as the boy sat down, and the chairman gave the floor to one of them, the same lad who had invited Mendeleyev to the meeting.

"I would like to call to the chairman's attention that we have among us tonight a man who has the very qualifications which the previous speaker mentioned," he said in a clear ringing voice. "I am referring to a scientist known throughout the world for his monumental discovery which has transformed modern chemistry. I am referring to Dmitri Ivanovitch Mendeleyev!"

Mendeleyev scowled. So he had been tricked! Could they think him such a fool as not to realize that asking him to the meeting had been part of a premeditated plan? Flattering to be sure, but he would have none of it.

"Dmitri Ivanovitch Mendeleyev," the youthful chairman was saying. "We, the students of the University of St. Petersburg, ask you, no, entreat you, to present our petition to the Minister of Education."

Slowly he rose to his feet.

"You all know my convictions. I am an evolutionist of a peaceful type. I like to see you at your books or doing experiments in the laboratory. How can you advance science by waving placards and shouting and passing your time making up petitions to the Minister of Education? You are here to study and that is what you should do."

Only after he sat down did he realize he had not absolutely refused to take their petition.

On the platform, the chairman conferred briefly with several other students. Then he turned to the assembly, addressing Mendeleyev directly.

"Dmitri Ivanovitch, we will make a bargain with you. If you will do us this one favor, we will return to our classes and work as we have never worked before."

There was a hushed silence, as Mendeleyev wrestled with himself.

"Agreed!" he bellowed suddenly.

He could not say whether he was doing right or wrong, or being wise or unwise, but the grateful looks the students gave him tore at his heart.

Two days later he went to the house of the Minister of Education, carrying the student petition and a brief personal note of explanation. Delyanov was out; he left the missives with a maid. He had no illusions that the petition would cause the Minister to change his ways, but he felt strangely pleased at having made the gesture.

That same afternoon a messenger brought back the unopened envelope containing the petition, with a brief message:

"On the instruction of the Minister of Education," it read, "the enclosed document is returned to Councilor of State Professor Mendeleyev, since neither the Minister nor anyone else in the service of His Imperial Majesty has the right to accept a document of this nature."

Flames of indignation seared his brain as he read the curt document. After this flagrant insult he had no choice. There was only one thing left for him to do.

The next morning he wrote out his resignation as professor in the universities of Russia.

The rector of the university came and pleaded with him to reconsider. His colleagues urged him to stay on, using every argument they could devise or invent. His students visited him in groups and singly, solemn and heartbroken. Would he not change his mind? They needed him.

He shook his head sadly. "It is no use. I can no longer breathe nor work in this atmosphere."

On March 22, he gave his last lecture. It was a long plea to make Russia strong through scientific knowledge. At his request, there was no applause. The students sat in silence as he left the hall for the last time.

The Mendeleyevs moved to a new apartment far from the university. Anna fixed it up prettily, saying how wonderful it was to have different surroundings, to be able to decorate her own home the way she liked. Even with the loss of the university salary, they had no serious money problems. His

outside earnings were sufficient to live on and take care of
Feozva too. There was no reason why he should not take
a long and needed rest.

But no sooner were they settled than he began to suffer
moods of dark depression. Since the age of fifteen, the
University of St. Petersburg had been his home, his family,
his life. He had learned from it and in return had given
it more than thirty years of dedicated labor. Desperately
he missed his students, his colleagues, the university atmosphere and scientific gossip. His resignation had been
a major operation. Only now did he experience the full
shock of it.

He had no heart to open a book, write a paper, perform
an experiment or even play with his children. Until late at
night he sat by himself in his unlighted study. Anna suffered with him and for him, and one evening when she
could bear it no longer, she came in and sat by his side.

"Would you like to talk about it, Mitenka?"

"What is there to say? I am sick—with a sickness not of
the body but of the soul. There is no cure for such a malady."

"You are quite wrong, my darling. For you, there is always
a cure."

"What do you mean? What cure?"

"The one you have always used. Work."

"Work? I have no feeling for it."

"You will have."

The next morning when he went into his study he found
that Anna had unpacked a box containing his papers and left
them on his table. A little later she opened his door quietly
and looked in. He was at his desk and his pen was moving.
She left without saying a word.

Legacy of Thoughts, he called this new opus, and beneath
the title he wrote: "Work; look for peace and calm in work,

you will find it nowhere else! Pleasures flit by—they are only for yourself; work leaves a mark of long lasting joy, work is for others."

Presently he took this embryo manuscript and put it away in a drawer. There was time enough to continue *Legacy of Thoughts* when he was an old man and could do nothing but philosophize. Suddenly he was wildly impatient to get back to science.

As he had done in his university apartment, he fitted up a room as a laboratory. He did experiments. Articles under his name once more appeared in the *Journal* of the Russian Chemical Society: "On the Analogy of the Dissolved Silver of Carey Lea with the Colloidal Constitution of Several Bodies"; "Regarding the Discovery of N_3H Family of Acids"; "The Change in the Density of Water Due to Heating."

The Russian Admiralty, either unaware or indifferent to the cloud under which he had left the university, approached him to develop an improved smokeless gunpowder. He plunged energetically into this project and within a year had succeeded. When the first tests were made on Mendeleyev's "pyrocollodion," it proved superior to most foreign smokeless gunpowders, in both speed and evenness of combustion.

Russia's Minister of Finance at this time was Sergei Witte, a man of extraordinary strength of character and ability. He had launched the Trans-Siberian Railroad and, in spite of the Tsar's *laissez-faire* policies, had taken mammoth steps to overhaul Russia's sinking economy. Witte was familiar with Mendeleyev's contributions to Russian industry and agriculture and was impressed with his work for the Admiralty. He had also made it his business to acquaint himself fully with the reasons behind the scientist's resignation from the University of St. Petersburg and felt that he had been treated disgracefully. In 1893, Witte appointed him Director of the Russian Bureau of Weights and Measures.

The family moved once more, this time to a third floor apartment of one of the bureau's buildings.

14

A LEGACY FOR THE FUTURE

"WEIGHTS AND MEASURES," MENDELEYEV EXPLAINED TO HIS wife and children, "are the principal instruments of our knowledge of nature. To be Director of the Bureau of Weights and Measures is to be responsible for those instruments. My job is not to be sneezed at."

With the enthusiasm and drive of a young man, he undertook to bring order to the chaos of existing systems of measurements in Russia. He utilized techniques developed in Germany, England and the United States, and invented new measuring devices himself. From abroad, he ordered laboratory furnaces, batteries and refrigeration machines. He established the metric system, which was not then obligatory in Russia, and insisted on an accuracy and precision of all measuring equipment never before enforced.

Finding that his employees were housed in wretched lodgings, he stormed the authorities with letters, petitions and personal visits until modern and sanitary apartments were built for them. Breaking precedent, he employed women as well as men, and bragged to his friends that some of his women proved superior to their male counterparts, so far as their work was concerned.

Foreign countries continued to pour honors on him. Among them were two honorary degrees from Cambridge and

Oxford, which he received in 1894, when he was sixty. For the ceremonies, he and Anna went once again to England. At Cambridge he meekly agreed to wear a red academic robe with blue trimming, and looked so picturesque that the English nicknamed him "Faust." He made another trip to England the next year, this time to receive the Copley Medal, granted him by the London Royal Society, the highest honor they had to offer him.

In 1899, his own government called on him again. Since he had done so well with oil and coal, would he now go to the Ural Mountains and study the iron industry? He spent a month there and accumulated enough material to write an 866-page book, *The Iron Industry of the Urals in the Year 1899.* The book was like the fulfillment of a pledge to the memory of Bassargin, who had first told him of the hidden wealth within those mountains.

That decade of the 1890's was one of notable scientific events outside of Russia. In 1895, a German professor, William Roentgen, discovered certain invisible rays which were so penetrating they could go through substances impervious to light. He called them X rays, the "X" standing for their unknown quality.

The next year, Henri Becquerel, a French professor, found other invisible rays emanating from uranium salts. A Polish-born young woman, Marie Curie, called this phenomenon "radioactivity" and by means of an electrometer detected radioactive radium and polonium, two new elements, in pitchblende ore.

In the meantime, J. J. Thomson, of Cambridge University, had discovered that atoms were not indivisible—that all of them contained minute negative corpuscles (later called electrons), with a mass less than a thousandth of that of the hydrogen atom.

Sensational as these developments were, Mendeleyev took the most personal interest in a chain of discoveries begun by his friend, Sir William Ramsay, working in collaboration with Lord W. S. Rayleigh. In 1895, they found in atmospheric nitrogen a hitherto undetected gas with red and green lines in its spectrum. Because this gas would not combine with other elements to form compounds, they named it argon, after the Greek word for "inert." The following year, in a spectrum analysis of the mineral cleveite, they came across the strong yellow line of helium, which had been identified on the sun but not on earth. This too was a gas, with an atomic weight about four times that of hydrogen, making it the next lightest of the elements. Like argon, it would not form chemical compounds.

The finding of two inert gaseous elements struck Ramsay as more than coincidental, and he started looking for others. With another collaborator, Morris William Travers, he found neon, krypton and xenon, all of which had similar characteristics.

"I did not doubt for a minute the full correctness of the periodic law," Ramsay wrote to the French Academy of Science. "I was convinced that in the system of my friend, Mendeleyev, there must be found a little place for the inert gases too."

"Most unsocial," commented Mendeleyev, reading of these new elements. "The gases are so snobbish they turn up their noses at every other element."

Neither he nor anyone else had guessed of the existence of the inert gases, but once they were found, the Russian scientist knew they must fit into the periodic table.

In 1902, he prepared a revised version of the table, giving Ramsay's five gases a column of their own. "Group 0," he called this column, "substances which do not combine with anything." He also found a spot for Madame Curie's radio-active radium, in Group II, headed by beryllium and magnesium, and classified as "alkali earths." There were now a total of 71 elements filling up the spaces once left blank, with room for still more.

In this new table, he used the revised standard of the atomic weight scale, by which comparisons of atomic weights were based not on hydrogen (with a fixed atomic weight of 1), as in his earlier ones, but on oxygen, given a fixed atomic weight of 16. Improved techniques had shown that hydrogen was a trifle more than one-sixteenth the weight of oxygen; its latest atomic weight was 1.008. There were other changes in line with recent scientific findings.

The world was catching up with the periodic table. What had seemed in 1869 no more than a daring but controversial theory was now accepted as a valuable tool by chemists everywhere.

Mendeleyev's interests were still as varied as ever. Resuming his old habits, he worked late in his study, night after night, writing now on one subject, now on another.

The problem of increasing population became one of his concerns. There were at this time an estimated 1.6 billion people in the world. In time he foresaw that this number would be doubled, tripled, quadrupled. How to feed them? He predicted that by fully utilizing scientific knowledge in improved agricultural techniques, the earth could easily supply subsistence to ten billion inhabitants.

He worked on a huge and comprehensive map of Russia, showing locations of cities, population distribution, wooded and barren areas, more accurate than any that had preceded it.

He expanded an idea that had first struck him on his visit

to the coal region of the Donets when he saw the hard and dangerous underworld life of the coal miners.

"There will be a time when coal will not be extracted from the earth," he wrote, "but will be converted underground into combustible gases which will be distributed over vast areas through pipes." He realized that for the present such a plan was not feasible, but put down his ideas as a legacy for future generations of scientists to ponder.

He turned his attention to the ether that filled all unoccupied space in the universe. *In an Attempt Toward a Chemical Conception of Ether* put forth the theory that ether was an element, with atoms, even lighter than hydrogen atoms, which traveled at incredible velocity. Those who held that ether had no material substance scoffed at his theory, but one American chemist baldly stated that this was the greatest discovery since the periodic law. For Mendeleyev, it was not a discovery but a hypothesis—which also would await the findings of future scientists.

"The greater a man's natural gifts, the greater his responsibility to society." Consciously or unconsciously, what he sought to do in these later writings was to probe the depths of his fertile, restless mind, and draw from it material which might inspire his successors.

On and on he wrote until, in spite of the brightness of the two oil lamps, everything seemed to go dim. On his study walls hung Anna's sketches of great and famous men—the musicians Beethoven, Wagner and Glinka; the painter Raphael; the philosopher Descartes; Shakespeare; Copernicus; Newton; Galileo, and his own colleagues, Menshutkin and Butelerov. One night he looked up at these familiar companions and found that their faces too were blurred.

The next morning as he went down the stairs he stumbled and fell.

Anna was at his side in a moment to help him up.

"A stupid miscalculation," he said, brushing his jacket.

But she had noticed other uncertainties in his movements and insisted he see a doctor.

For a man of sixty-seven, his health was superb, the doctor said, after a thorough examination. "Except for your eyes. You'll have to take care. Rest more. Avoid close work."

Obstinately, he continued to work nights as he had always done, but he had to hold a magnifying glass with his left hand so he could see the words he set down.

Anna brought in a foreign eye specialist. This pompous man diagnosed that the "inner fluid" of Mendeleyev's eyes was "deteriorating." Within at least three months, he prophesied, he would be totally blind.

With even more desperate haste, Mendeleyev went on with his writing.

They had a physician friend, Dr. Kostenitch, who refused to accept the foreign specialist's verdict. "Your father had cataracts on his eyes, and he recovered his sight through an operation. You too can be cured."

When they told the foreign specialist what Kostenitch had said, he told them coldly that an operation would result in immediate loss of sight.

"Three months? Now? What is the difference?" demanded Mendeleyev.

Dr. Kostenitch performed the operation in Mendeleyev's study. For two weeks thereafter he wore bandages over his eyes. Kostenitch with his assistant returned to take them off. Only then would they know if the operation was a success.

"I want Anna here," Mendeleyev said. "I want the children in the next room."

The assistant cut the bandages and Kostenitch removed

them gently. Mendeleyev blinked and looked up to see his wife.

"*Akh*, I had forgotten how beautiful you were," he told her.

Then the children rushed in and smothered him with caresses.

To the men and women employees of the Bureau of Weights and Measures, Mendeleyev, their chief, was known simply as *he*. "*He* is not afraid of anybody," they said. Or, "*He* is busy with a new project."

He was a tall stooped figure with a massive head, high forehead, white beard and near-shoulder-length white locks. *He* was a man of science who had written over five hundred works—some more than a thousand pages long—not to mention all his other achievements. *He* was someone who could roar like a lion at inefficiency and bureaucracy, yet was capable of infinite gentleness. It was not unusual for him to blast a man for some careless error and the next moment humbly beg his pardon for offending him.

Over the years Mendeleyev won a fervid loyalty from his staff. His sorrows and joys were theirs too. They wept with him at the death of his first-born son, Volodya, a thirty-four-year-old officer in the Marine Corps with his whole life before him. They rejoiced when his daughter Liubov married the poet Alexander Alexandrovitch Blok, a marriage of love for the young girl whose name meant "love."

Behind his back they talked about his rages, his kindness, his idiosyncrasies, and repeated the legends that had grown up around him.

Russia's greatest scientist, of all things, was hopelessly superstitious. Seven was lucky and thirteen unlucky. Nothing could change his mind on that score. No important work at the bureau could be started on the thirteenth of the month, nor did he travel on that day if he could possibly avoid it.

Once after a scientific conference in Paris, through an oversight he left for St. Petersburg on the thirteenth. He arrived two days late, beside himself with disgust and indignation. At Berlin, where he had to change trains, the porter left him in the waiting room, promising to call him when his train arrived. Before the porter returned he looked through the window and saw a train marked "St. Petersburg–Paris." He grabbed his baggage and managed to get on just as the train pulled out. Six hours later the conductor re-examined his ticket.

"Your ticket is for St. Petersburg, your excellency. This train is headed for Paris."

He had to pay for the trip he had made in error, get out at the next station, spend a night in a strange place, and then buy another ticket back to Berlin, where he caught the next train for St. Petersburg.

All because he had left Paris originally on the thirteenth!

The Director of the Bureau of Weights and Measures liked farmers, with whom he could talk about farming, or workingmen and skilled laborers, with whom he could discuss problems connected with their work. On occasion he did not mind talking economics with businessmen. But he had a distinct aversion toward newspapermen, whose strange profession was beyond his comprehension.

Reporters were always arriving at the bureau to try and get an interview with the Director. Usually his secretary, Olga Ozarovskaya, or his servant, Mikhaila, nicknamed "Fish Hook" by the staff, was able to keep the intruders away. One day, Fish Hook was off on an errand and Olga was in the Director's office taking dictation—a letter to a Spanish chemist who had prepared a new iodine compound which

Mendeleyev believed warranted a re-examination of iodine's atomic weight.

In the midst of it, a stranger knocked and entered without waiting for an answer.

"Who are you?" Mendeleyev demanded, glowering.

"A reporter from the St. Petersburg *Listok*, your excellency." The stranger bowed.

"Dmitri Ivanovitch," Mendeleyev corrected him. "Well, what is it?"

"My paper thought—that is, if your excellency—" the reporter stammered.

"Dmitri Ivanovitch!" Mendeleyev's voice rose to a roar.

"I have come, your excellen—"

"Dmitri Ivanovitch!!!"

The reporter finally grasped that Mendeleyev was one man who did not like titles.

"I wish to deprive you of only a few minutes, Dmitri Ivanovitch."

"All right, but hurry. We are writing a letter."

The reporter dropped into the haven of an easy chair. "If you please, what do you think of radio?"

"You have come here just to ask me *that?*" Mendeleyev demanded in astonishment. "Never mind, I have an article on the subject." There were very few scientific subjects on which he had not written. He signaled Olga to fetch this one from his files. "Is that all?"

The reporter clung to the chair as if fearing eviction. "How did you come to think of the periodic table, Dmitri Ivanovitch?"

In spite of all he had written about the origin of the table, people still plagued him with that question. He could not bear it.

"I did not do it at so many kopeks per line," he said,

scathingly. "It did not come to me all of a sudden. I thought about it twenty years. Now, will you go? We have to finish our letter."

The reporter made one more effort to draw out his subject. "What sort of letter are you writing, Dmitri Ivanovitch?"

Mendeleyev froze. "A love letter! What else?" he thundered. "Now, leave."

The reporter, realizing how he had blundered, blushed, muttered apologies, and made for the door.

Seeing his dejection, Mendeleyev suddenly relented, called him back, and in simple language explained about the iodine compound with which the letter was concerned. But after the reporter was gone, he put his head in his arms and muttered, "Why, why, do they pester me? The man understood nothing."

His seventieth birthday in 1904 was officially proclaimed as the day of the Fiftieth Jubilee, since he had given fifty years to the service of Russian science. His office desk overflowed with telegrams and letters of congratulation. They came from the universities that had given him honorary degrees, from the Royal Society of London and foreign academies of sciences that had elected him to membership, and from innumerable other scientific organizations. They came from his scientific colleagues and friends all over the world.

"What am I to do with them?" he asked Olga, his secretary.

"You might insert an announcement in the newspapers, saying you wish to express your thanks to all of them that way, since you cannot reply personally," Olga suggested. "It is quite customary."

"I will do no such thing," he snorted. "That is no way to treat one's friends."

She knew he would answer them all himself, even though it took months.

The employees of the Bureau of Weights and Measures held a reception for him. In the traditional manner of laboratories, they drank hot chocolate in beakers instead of cups, used glass rods for spoons, and filter paper as napkins. Mendeleyev left the party at its height. At home he was expecting to receive a stream of delegations.

"All this fuss," he complained to Anna. "All the speeches to be read. What a nuisance! I'm an old man and no longer have time for this sort of thing."

Nevertheless he was polite to all their visitors, as she knew he would be, even the delegate of the Imperial Academy of Science. Though this body had never seen fit to make him a member, their delegate spoke at length and pompously of the "important contribution to Russian science of the Father of the Periodic Table."

"So," gloated Mendeleyev when he left, "they think they can convince me that the academy is no longer self-satisfied in its great sepulchral dignity?"

Later Olga arrived, bringing flowers from the women workers of the Bureau of Weights and Measures.

"These are our token of thanks, Dmitri Ivanovitch," she said. "We want them also to express the gratitude of all the Russian women whom you admitted to your classes when no one else would."

"*Akh*, from the girls?" he demanded, pleased. "They must be put in water at once." He went into the kitchen himself to get a vase for them.

"You did not mind too much?" Anna asked at the end of the day.

"Of course, I minded," he grumbled. "Such a waste of time!"

Then he smiled and laid his hand over hers. "*Akh,* how lovely you are."

Anna, at forty-five with four grown children, was still a handsome woman. To her husband she would always be the golden-haired girl with whom he had fallen in love. Over the years, her grace and charm had given his own life a special meaning. Her innate common sense had made bearable even a Fiftieth Jubilee.

Russia was at war again that year, this time with the Japanese, a costly futile struggle which had begun in February 1904 because the Japanese resented Russian penetration of Manchuria and North Korea. The quick victory of which Nicolas II, the Tsar since 1896, was so confident did not happen. Russia suffered repeated and prestige-damaging defeats until peace was made in September 1905 through the mediation of the American President, Theodore Roosevelt.

Long before, the Russian people had grown tired of suffering privations for a war they did not want and could not understand. On January 22, 1905, some two hundred thousand men, women and children, led by a priest, marched to the Winter Palace to present a petition. They protested starvation wages, and asked for an eight-hour day, freedom for political prisoners, a national assembly, and a constitution.

The Tsar, a man who liked to avoid trouble, was not there. When the big square in front of the palace was filled with petitioners, the soldiers of the palace guard opened fire. More than five hundred were killed and several thousand wounded. The survivors remembered most clearly the blood on the snow. "Bloody Sunday" marked the beginning of a crescendo in strikes, demonstrations and acts of terrorism, a rumbling prelude to the gigantic upheaval of a revolution which Mendeleyev would not live to see.

His favorite diversion in these years when his eyes tired quickly was to have Anna read to him. His favorites were Jules Verne's science fantasies, James Fenimore Cooper's stories of American Indians, Russian poetry, Victor Hugo's *The Octopus*, the adventure novels of Alexandre Dumas.

One day Anna read a passage from Dumas: "At this instant the knight rose, swept out his sword, and six soldiers lay dead on the tavern floor."

"Very good," he commented dryly. "In our literature one person is killed and there are two volumes of suffering, but here on one page, six men are killed and no one has regrets."

In the fall of 1906, he had an attack of influenza. To recuperate he went to Cannes in southern France, relaxing in the dazzling blues of the Mediterranean sky and water and the tropical heat of the sun. He felt fine on his return, but soon afterward the symptoms of his illness returned to plague him.

The Minister of Commerce and Industry, D. A. Filosofov, paid a visit to the Bureau of Weights and Measures on January 11, 1907. The Director escorted his eminent guest personally on a tour of the offices and laboratories. In a room where an open window let in a strong draft of air, the two men stood talking. Mendeleyev arrived home chilled and shaking.

Vainly Anna tried to get him to stay in bed for a few days. Stubborn as always, he kept to his regular schedule, going to the bureau in the daytime and at night revising his latest book, *Toward an Increase of Knowledge of Russia,* a complete plan of commercial and industrial development, based on his intimate knowledge of Russia's resources in raw materials and in scientific skills.

Nadezhda, now a married woman with a family of her

own, came to see him one evening and found him sitting at
his desk his pen in his hand, as she had seen him so many
times before. But never had he looked at her with such a
strange faraway expression.

"You're not feeling well, Uncle. You'd better lie down."

"It's nothing." He reached for a cigarette but his hand
trembled so he could not light it.

"Maybe you should not smoke."

"Ridiculous," he barked. "Here, you light it for me."

She handed back the lighted cigarette, and he took a
contented puff. "When I stop smoking then you'll know it's
all over for me, Mashenka," he said, using his old pet name
for her.

The next day he could not get out of bed. He was so
drowsy he seemed hardly aware of the presence of Anna
or the doctor who diagnosed his illness as pneumonia.

Many visitors came to his door the next few days. He
recognized only a few of those who were admitted. Once
in a while the whispered comments of his family reached
him from outside the door.

"His pallor, Mother, it's frightening," he heard his daughter
Liubov say. "Oh, I do love him so."

At one o'clock the morning of January 20, he woke up
suddenly and asked Anna to bring him some warm milk. He
drank only a few sips, then sank back on his pillow.

"Read to me, darling."

"What would you like?"

"Jules Verne. *The English at the North Pole.* At one
time, I too wanted to go to the North Pole. Life is so full
of so many things. A pity no one man can do them all."

It was five o'clock in the morning when she stopped reading. He had fallen into his last sleep.

On January 25, Mendeleyev was buried at Volkovo Cemetery, where also rested his mother, his sisters Liza and Ekaterina, and Volodya, his first-born son. In the funeral procession his friends, his colleagues and important government officials walked beside humble working people and muzhiks who had come from Boblovo and Klin and other parts of Russia. There were also thousands of high school and university students, girls and youths. Two of them carried a great tablet marked with the Periodic Table.

In the frosty dawn the street lamps of St. Petersburg, draped in black crepe, burned wanly. A city and a nation paid homage to a man of humanity and a man of science.

EPILOGUE

IN THE YEARS FOLLOWING MENDELEYEV'S DEATH, SCIENTISTS all over the world joined Marie Curie in investigating radioactivity and radioactive elements, their task made easier because of the now universally accepted principle of the periodic table. A New Zealand physicist, Ernest Rutherford, devised a method of using rays from radioactive substances as "bullets" to explore the mystery of the atom. In 1913, when he was a professor at England's University of Manchester, Rutherford announced that all atoms of all elements had a minute core or nucleus with a positive electrical charge, and that negatively charged electrons were distributed in the rest of the area of the atom. This major discovery obliterated forever the nineteenth-century conception of an atom as a tiny solid.

One of Rutherford's researchers at this time was a slim dark-haired young man named Henry Moseley, who was engaged on a seemingly unrelated project. This was a study of the diffraction of X rays in their passage through rock crystal. In the course of this work he succeeded in taking a photograph of the spectrum of the X rays, the first time this had been done.

He produced his X rays by directing a stream of negative electrons against a positively charged metal plate. X rays do not all have the same wavelengths. When Moseley used different metals in the charged plates, the resulting X rays had different wavelengths. From this he reasoned that possibly every element had a different X ray spectrum.

To test this theory, using a variety of techniques which he invented, he proceeded to get photographs of X ray spectra, first of metallic elements, then of nonmetallic. From these experiments he observed that though every element had an X ray spectrum of two strong lines, the characteristic X ray wavelength increased, in a regular manner, with the atomic weight of the element!

"There is a fundamental quality in the atom which increases by regular steps as we pass from one element to the next," he wrote.

This "fundamental quality" was the positive charge of the atom nucleus, to which Rutherford gave the name "proton."

Up through the lifetime of Mendeleyev, elements were listed in order of their atomic weight. This method proved increasingly cumbersome as more accurate measuring instruments produced more fractions in the atomic weight figures. By Moseley's "law of atomic numbers," elements fell neatly in order by the number of protons in the nuclei of their atoms.

Hydrogen, which had one proton in the atom nucleus, became atomic number 1. Helium, with two protons, became atomic number 2. And so on with the increase of one proton per element up to uranium, which had 92 protons, and became atomic number 92. With uranium, the periodic table was full, so far as it went.

With one exception, the order of the elements by the atomic weight scale and the atomic number scale was identical. Tellurium has an atomic weight of 127.16 and iodine an atomic weight of 126.92. Mendeleyev had long insisted that tellurium must come before iodine in the periodic table. By Moseley's law of atomic numbers, the atomic number of tellurium was 52 and iodine 53, and they fell into their proper places in the table. The reason for the discrepancy in atomic weights was later explained by the presence of other particles in the atoms. Mendeleyev was once more proved a prophet of amazing ability.

The beautiful order of Moseley's law of atomic numbers delighted the scientific world. It was a pity that Mendeleyev could not have lived to see this remarkable proof of the "harmony of nature."

In the next several years, new discoveries threw light on the mystery of why certain elements, at regular intervals in the atomic weight scale—and the atomic number scale—were similar.

The proton had a mass approximately 2000 times that of the electron, but their opposite electric charges provided a balance. Each atom had the same number of protons and electrons. Hydrogen had one electron whirling around its single proton nucleus, and uranium had ninety-two electrons revolving about its heavy nucleus of ninety-two protons.

The electrons revolved in orbits, or shells. The shell nearest the nucleus could hold just two electrons. The second shell could hold eight electrons, the third, eighteen, and the fourth, thirty-two. In accordance with what proportion these shells were filled to capacity depended the valency of the element, the phenomenon Mendeleyev had first called "atomicity."

When atoms get together to form molecules, they loan, borrow or share electrons from their outer shells.

The inert gases (Group 0 in the periodic table)—helium, neon, argon, krypton, xenon, radon—have atomic numbers respectively of 2, 10, 18, 36, 54 and 86. All the outer shells of their atoms are comfortably filled. That is why they do not form compounds with other elements.

Lithium, sodium and potassium (one of Doebereiner's triads and all in Group I of the periodic table) have atomic numbers of 3, 11 and 19. In all three the outer shell has only one electron. When their atoms form molecules, they loan their single electron to atoms of other elements.

Fluorine, chlorine, bromine, iodine (Group VII), with atomic numbers of 9, 17, 35, 53, all have seven electrons in the outer shells of their atoms. They "borrow" an electron to form a molecule.

It was as though every atom was driven by instinct to get rid of electrons or to collect electrons, so that its outer shell would be stabilized.

Scientists had long known that carbon (Group IV) was quadrivalent, that is, that it had a valency of four. Now a reason was found. Carbon, atomic number 6, has two electrons in its inner shell and four in its outer shell. To complete this outer shell to eight, it needs four more electrons. The tightly bound molecule of methane gas, CH_4, has one carbon atom and four hydrogen atoms. The carbon atom, so to speak, takes the four hydrogen atoms hostage, and forces them to pay tribute of their four electrons.

In every case, the chemical characteristics of an element depend upon the number of electrons in the outer shell of its atoms.

One of the most puzzling group of elements are the rare earths, which form the lanthanine series in the modern periodic table. The rare earths begin with lanthanum, atomic number 57, and run in sequence up to and including lutecium, atomic number 71. All have similar chemical characteristics. They had proved a stumbling block to

Mendeleyev and to everyone else up until the structure of the atom was revealed. All these elements have the same place in the periodic table under Group III. All have two electrons in their outer shells. Unlike other elements, as their atomic numbers increase, they add the additional electrons to their *inner* shells instead of the outer ones.

All man's knowledge of the intricate atomic structure and behavior patterns of the electrons stemmed from the discovery of radioactivity in 1897. Because of knowledge of radioactivity, men were able to develop new tools to explore the atom. But all the ingenious experiments, complex mathematical calculations and theoretical deductions involved in this exploration were made easier by the periodic table of the elements, conceived by Mendeleyev and perfected by Henry Moseley.

The story of the elements was not yet ended.

There was the technique by which men learned to bombard atoms with atomic particles and turn them into atoms of other elements—even radioactive ones. There was the creation of artificial isotopes, with their many uses for industry, medicine and agriculture. There was the discovery of a third particle of the atom, the neutron, which had nearly the same mass as a proton, but no electric charge. There was eventually nuclear fission, the splitting of the atom by a direct hit of the tiny neutron on the atom nucleus, causing the release of an incredibly vast amount of energy which could be used for destruction or for technological progress.

Another phenomenon was produced by neutron bombardment—the creation of elements with atomic numbers higher than that of uranium, elements that had never been known on earth.

To date, there are eleven of these man-made "transuranic"

INDEX

About the Author

ROBIN McKOWN was born in Denver, Colorado. Her first literary success came at the University of Colorado where her one-act play won first prize in a local contest. She studied for a year at Northwestern's School of Drama, and took classes in short story writing at the University of Illinois. She has written radio scripts, a book and author column for a newspaper, did public relations and has been an author's agent. Her first full length book was such a challenging and rewarding experience, she is now devoting all of her time to books for young people and adults. Mrs. McKown makes her home in New York City.